EDEXCEL
BIOLOGY 2

A-Level Year 2/A Level

MODEL
ANSWERS

This model answer booklet is a companion publication to provide answers for the activities in the EDEXCEL Biology 2 Student Workbook. These answers have been produced as a separate publication to keep the cost of the workbook itself to a minimum. All answers to set questions are provided, but chapter reviews are the student's own and no model answer is set. Working and explanatory notes have been provided where clarification of the answer is appropriate.

ISBN 978-1-927309-28-5

Copyright © 2017 Richard Allan
Published and printed by BIOZONE Learning (UK) Ltd

PHOTOCOPYING PROHIBITED

including photocopying under a photocopy licence scheme such as CLA

Additional copies of this Model Answers book may be purchased directly from the publisher.

BIOZONE Learning Media (UK) Ltd.

Telephone local:	01283 530 366
Telephone international:	+44 1283 530 366
Fax local:	01283 831 900
Fax international:	+44 1283 831 900
Email:	sales@biozone.co.uk

www.**BIOZONE**.co.uk

CONTENTS EDEXCEL BIOLOGY 1

Energy for biological processes

1	The Role of ATP In Cells	4
2	ATP Production in Cells	4
3	The Biochemistry of Respiration	4
4	Chemiosmosis	4
5	Anaerobic Pathways	4
6	Factors Affecting Respiration Rate	4
7	Energy Transformations in Plant Cells	5
8	Pigments and Light Absorption	5
9	How Does Wavelength Affect Photosynthesis?	5
10	Separation of Pigments by Chromatography	5
11	Photosynthesis	5
12	Chloroplasts	5
13	Light Dependent Reactions	5
14	Light Independent Reactions	6
14	Experimental Investigation of Photosynthesis	6
16	Investigating Enzymes in Photosynthesis	6
17	The Fate of Triose Phosphate	6
18	Factors Affecting Photosynthesis	6
19	Investigating Photosynthetic Rate	7
20	Overcoming Limiting Factors in Photosynthesis	7
21	Chapter Review	7
22	KEY TERMS AND IDEAS: Did You Get It?	7

Microbiology and pathogens

23	Culturing Microorganisms	7
24	Dilution Plating	7
25	Investigating Bacterial Growth	8
26	Strain Isolation	8
27	Isolating a Bacterial Species	8
28	Microbial Growth Curve	8
29	Plotting Microbial Growth	8
30	Bacterial Pathogens	8
31	Antibiotics	9
32	The Evolution of Antibiotic Resistance	9
33	The Implications of Antibiotic Resistance	9
34	Fungi, Viruses, and Protozoan Pathogens	9
35	Stem Rust Fungus	9
36	The Influenza Virus	9
37	Malaria	9
38	Malaria is Endemic in Some Countries	10
39	The Body's Defences	10
40	The Innate Immune Response	10
41	Phagocytes and Phagocytosis	10
42	Processing Antigens	10
43	The Lymphatic System	10
44	The Adaptive Immune System	11
45	Clonal Selection	11
46	Antibodies	11
47	Acquired Immunity	11
48	Vaccines and Vaccination	11
49	Vaccines Can Eliminate Infectious Disease	11
50	Questions About Vaccines	12
51	Chapter Review	12
52	KEY TERMS AND IDEAS: Did You Get It?	12

Modern genetics

53	Genomes	12
54	PCR and Modern Genetics	12
55	Applications of Gene Sequencing	12
56	Gene Sequencing and Medicine	12
57	DNA Profiling	12
58	Forensic Applications of DNA Profiling	13
59	Gene Expression Overview	13
60	Transcription Factors Control Gene Expression	13
61	mRNA Processing	13
62	DNA Packaging and Transcription	13
63	The Effect of DNA Methylation	13
64	Non-Coding RNA Can Silence Gene Expression	13
65	What are Stem Cells?	13
66	Epigenetic Factors Regulate Cell Differentiation	14
67	Stem Cells and the Treatment of Disease	14
68	Making Recombinant DNA	14
69	Transgenic Organisms	14
70	Vectors for Transgenesis	14
71	Plasmids and Gene Cloning	14
72	Determining Gene Function with Knockout Mice	15
73	A Model Transgenic: Engineering Human Insulin	15
74	Genetic Modification of Soybeans	15
75	Engineering a Solution: Food for the Masses	15
76	Ethics of GMO Technology	16
77	Chapter Review	16
78	KEY TERMS AND IDEAS: Did You Get It?	16

Origins of genetic variation

79	Sources of Genetic Variation	16
80	Alleles	17
81	Meiosis and Variation	17
82	The Monohybrid Cross	17
83	The Test Cross	17
84	Practising Monohybrid Crosses	17
85	Problems Involving Monohybrid Inheritance	18
86	Codominance of Alleles	18
87	Codominance in Multiple Allele Systems	18
88	Dihybrid Cross	18
89	Inheritance of Linked Genes	18
90	Recombination and Dihybrid Inheritance	19
91	Detecting Linkage in Dihybrid Inheritance	19
92	Chi-Squared in Genetics	19
93	Using Chi-Squared in Genetics	19
94	Problems Involving Dihybrid Inheritance	20
95	Sex Linked Genes	20
96	Inheritance Patterns	21
97	Pedigree Analysis	21
98	Gene Pools and Evolution	22
99	Changes in a Gene Pool	22
100	Hardy-Weinberg Calculations	22
101	Analysis of a Squirrel Gene Pool	23
102	Gene Pool Model	23
103	Modelling Natural Selection	23
104	Types of Natural Selection	23

CONTENTS EDEXCEL BIOLOGY 1

105   Stabilising Selection for Human Birth Weight 23
106   Directional Selection in Moths 24
107   Directional Selection in Darwin's Finches 24
108   Disruptive Selection in Darwin's Finches................ 24
109   Genetic Drift Affects Gene Pools........................... 24
110   The Founder Effect... 24
111   Genetic Bottlenecks 25
112   Chapter Review 25
113   KEY TERMS AND IDEAS: Did You Get It?............. 25

Control systems

114   Homeostasis... 25
115   Negative Feedback... 25
116   Positive Feedback 25
117   Hormonal Regulatory Systems 26
118   What is Signal Transduction? 26
119   Modes of Hormone Action...................................... 26
120   Auxins, Gibberellins, and Cytokinins 26
121   Plant Hormones as Signal Molecules 26
122   The Role of Auxins in Apical Dominance 26
123   How Gibberellins Affect Growth............................. 26
124   The Effect of Gibberellin on Amylase Production 27
125   Photoperiodism in Plants.. 27
126   The Mammalian Nervous System 27
127   The Autonomic Nervous System............................. 28
128   The Human Brain 28
129   Neurones 28
130   Transmission of Nerve Impulses 28
131   Synapses 28
132   Integration at Synapses... 29
133   Drugs at Synapses 29
134   The Basis of Sensory Perception 29
135   The Structure of the Eye 29
136   The Physiology of Vision 29
137   Extrinsic Control of Heartbeat 30
138   The Liver's Role in Protein Metabolism.................. 30
139   The Urinary System 30
140   The Physiology of the Kidney 30
141   Control of Urine Output 30
142   Adaptations for Conserving Water.......................... 31
143   Endothermy vs Ectothermy 31
144   Thermoregulation in Humans.................................. 31
145   The Role of the Skin in Thermoregulation............... 31
146   Chapter Review 31
147   KEY TERMS AND IDEAS: Did You Get It?............. 32

Ecosystems

148   Components of an Ecosystem 32
149   Types of Ecosystems 32
150   Habitat... 32
151   Food Chains 32
152   Food Webs 32
153   Ecological Pyramids... 32
154   Measuring Distribution and Abundance 33
155   Quadrat Sampling 33

156   Quadrat-Based Estimates 33
157   Transect Sampling... 33
158   Qualitative Practical Work: Seaweed Zonation 33
159   Sampling Technique and Population Estimates....... 34
160   Quantifying Variation Using Student's t-Test........... 35
161   Quantitative Investigation of Variation 36
162   Pearson's Linear Correlation 36
163   Spearman Rank Correlation.................................... 37
164   What is Primary Productivity? 37
165   Productivity and Trophic Efficiency 37
166   Energy Inputs and Outputs 37
167   Energy Budget in an Ecosystem 38
168   Nutrient Cycles 38
169   Nitrogen Cycle... 39
170   Carbon Cycle 39
171   Ecosystems are Dynamic 40
172   Ecosystem Changes 40
173   Primary Succession 40
174   Succession on Surtsey Island................................ 40
175   Secondary Succession... 40
176   Population Size and Carrying Capacity 41
177   A Case Study in Carrying Capacity........................ 41
179   Chi-Squared Exercise in Ecology........................... 41
180   Investigating Distribution and Abundance 41
181   Species Interactions 42
182   Interpreting Predator-Prey Relationships 42
183   Interspecific Competition....................................... 42
184   Niche Differentiation 42
185   Intraspecific Competition....................................... 42
186   Humans Depend on Ecosystems............................43
187   Human Sustainability..43
188   Human Impact on the Ocean 44
189   Overfishing 44
190   Sustainable Fishing 44
191   The Greenhouse Effect 44
192   Climate Change..44
193   The History of Climate Modelling 44
194   Models of Climate Change......................................46
195   Climate Change and Effects on Biodiversity 46
196   Climate Change and Agriculture 46
197   Climate Change and Effects on the Arctic..............46
198   Temperature and the Distribution of Species 46
199   Ocean Acidification...46
200   Technological Solutions for Climate Change...........47
201   Supporting Conservation Through Legislation 47
202   Chapter Review 47
203   KEY TERMS AND IDEAS: Did You Get It?..............47

NOTES 48

1. The Role of ATP in Cells (page 3)

1. Organisms need to respire so that the energy in food can be converted, via a series of reactions, into the energy yielding molecule, ATP, which powers metabolic reactions.

2. (a) Mitochondria are the site for the Krebs cycle and ETS stages of cell respiration and ATP production.
   (b) Compartmentalisation within the mitochondrion keeps all the required components for specific metabolic reactions in one place, increasing efficiency.

3. Maintaining body temperature (thermoregulation) is requires energy input. ATP is required for the muscular activity involved in shivering (used to heat the body). ATP is also required for the secretion of sweat (used to cool the body).

2. ATP Production in Cells (page 4)

1. (a) Glycolysis: cytoplasm
   (b) Link reaction: matrix of mitochondria
   (c) Krebs cycle: matrix of mitochondria
   (d) Electron transport chain: cristae (inner membrane surface) of mitochondria.

2. The ATP generated in glycolysis and the Krebs cycle is generated by substrate level phosphorylation, i.e. transfer of a phosphate group directly from a substrate to ADP. In contrast, the ATP generated via the electron transport chain is through oxidative phosphorylation, a step-wise series of redox reactions that provide the energy for forming ATP. Oxidative phosphorylation yields much more ATP per glucose than substrate level phosphorylation.

3. The Biochemistry of Respiration (page 5)

1.

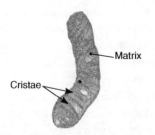

Matrix

Cristae

2. The link reaction prepares pyruvate for entry in the Krebs cycle. Carbon dioxide is removed and coenzyme A is added.

3. (a) 6   (b) 3   (c) 2   (d) 6   (e) 5   (f) 4

4. (a) Glycolysis: 2 ATPs
   (b) Krebs cycle: 2 ATPs
   (c) Electron transport chain: 34 ATPs
   (d) Total produced: 38 ATPs

5. The carbon atoms are lost as CO_2 molecules.

6. During oxidative phosphorylation, ADP is phosphorylated to ATP. Electrons passed along the electron transport chain are used to pump hydrogen ions across the inner membrane of the mitochondria. The flow of hydrogen ions back across the membrane is coupled to the phosphorylation of ADP to ATP. Oxygen is the final electron acceptor, reducing hydrogen to water. Oxygen is the final acceptor, so the process is called oxidative phosphorylation.

4. Chemiosmosis (page 7)

1. ATP synthesis is coupled to electron transport and movement of H^+. Energy from the transfer of electrons is used to pump protons (H^+), against their concentration gradient, into the intermembrane space, creating a high concentration of protons there. The protons return across the membrane down a concentration gradient via the enzyme complex, ATP synthase, which synthesises the ATP.

2. Elevating the H^+ concentration outside the exposed inner mitochondrial membranes would cause them to move down their concentration gradient via ATP synthase, generating ATP.

3. A suspension of isolated chloroplasts would become alkaline because protons would be removed from the medium as ATP was generated.

4. (a) By placing chloroplasts in an acid medium, the thylakoid interior was acidified. Transfer to an alkaline medium established a proton gradient from the thylakoid interior to the medium.
   (b) The protons could flow down the concentration gradient established, via ATP synthase, and generate ATP.

5. Anaerobic Pathways (page 8)

1. Aerobic respiration requires oxygen as the final electron acceptor whereas fermentation does not. [Also acceptable: Aerobic respiration produces a lot of ATP per glucose molecule. In fermentation the yield is lower].

2. Because the conversion of pyruvate to lactate is reversible, the lactate shuttle can regenerate pyruvate to supply Krebs cycle (aerobic cellular respiration)

3. Prolonged anaerobic metabolism leads to more of the muscle's ATP requirements being met by glycolysis. As a result, lactate accumulates faster than it can be oxidised and hydrogen ions accumulate (because the electron transport chain is not removing them fast enough). Pi accumulates from the breakdown of ATP (and creatine phosphate). This impairs calcium release and leads to a fall in ATP production. Both impair the muscle's ability to contract (fatigue).

4. (a) $2 \div 38 \times 100 = 5.3\%$ efficiency
   (b) Only a small amount of the energy of a glucose molecule is released in anaerobic respiration. The remainder stays locked up in the molecule.

5. (a) Root cells generate ATP anaerobically when deprived of oxygen, e.g. when growing in waterlogged soil. Alcholic fermentation is the only pathway available for ATP generation under these conditions.
   (b) Ethanol is toxic at higher concentrations. In most plants, it must be converted back to respiratory intermediates and respired aerobically. **Note**: this is why plants not adapted to waterlogged soils will eventually die.
   (c) Adaptations:
   – Removing the ethanol produced by fermentation with the enzyme alcohol dehydrogenase
   – Aerenchyma tissue with large air spaces that allow oxygen to be supplied to the root cells.

6. Factors Affecting Respiration Rate (page 10)

1. Oxygen is being used so the air pressure in the chamber is dropping, moving the bubble towards the chamber.

2. (a)

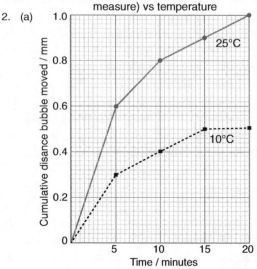

Respiration rate (indirect measure) vs temperature

25°C

10°C

Cumulative disance bubble moved / mm

Time / minutes

(b) Rate of oxygen consumption at 10°C:
   $0.5 \times 20\ \mu L = 10\ \mu L$ in 20 minutes for 5 seeds
   $= 0.1\ \mu L\ min^{-1}$ per seed

© 2017 **BIOZONE** International
ISBN: 978-1-927309-28-5
Photocopying Prohibited

(c) Rate of oxygen consumption at 25°C:
1.0 x 20 µL = 20 µL in 20 minutes for 5 seeds
= 0.20 µL min^{-1} per seed

(d) An increase in temperature from 10°C to 25°C increased the rate of respiration by 2.5 times.

3. The glass beads acted as a control to show that the difference in the results at the two temperatures was a result of processes within the pea seeds.

7. Energy Transformations in Plant Cells (page 11)

1. The hydrolysis of ATP is coupled to the formation of a reactive intermediate, which can do work. Effectively, the hydrolysis of ATP to ADP + Pi releases energy.

2. (a) Photosynthesis: Carbon dioxide and water.
   (b) Cellular respiration: Oxygen and glucose.

3. Glucose (or pyruvate).

4. Solar energy (the Sun).

5. Food (plants and other animals).

8. Pigments and Light Absorption (page 12)

1. The wavelength of the light spectrum absorbed by a pigment, e.g. chlorophyll absorbs red and blue light and appears green. **Note**: Represented graphically, the absorption spectrum shows the relative amounts of light absorbed at different wavelengths.

2. They absorb light wavelengths that chlorophyll *a* cannot absorb, and pass their energy on to chlorophyll *a*. **Note**: This broadens the action spectrum over which chlorophyll *a* can fuel photosynthesis.

9. How Does Wavelength Affect Photosynthesis? (page 13)

1. If red and blue wavelengths of light are most effective at driving photosysnthesis, leaf discs should photosynthesise faster and therefore float more quickly when exposed to these wavelengths than when exposed to green light.

2. As the leaf discs photosynthesise, they produce oxygen, which accumulates within the leaf tissue and makes the discs buoyant.

3. (a)

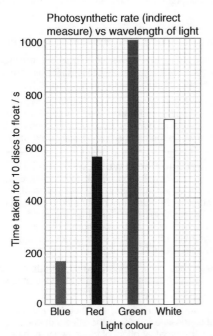

Photosynthetic rate (indirect measure) vs wavelength of light

(b) Blue light was most effective at driving photosynthesis because the discs illuminated with blue light were the quickest to float (more oxygen produced per unit time). This was followed by red light, then white light. Green light

(reflected by leaves) was poor at driving photosynthesis.

4. Yes, as predicted, photosynthetic rate was highest at red and blue light wavelengths (as measured by time for discs to float) and lowest in green light.

10. Separation of Pigments by Chromatography (page 14)

1. (a) and (b)

A: Rf value 0.92. Pigment: carotene
B: Rf value 0.53. Pigment: chlorophyll a
C: Rf value: 0.46. Pigment: chlorophyll b
   *Note: exact replication of the Rf values may not always occur. In this example, Chlorophyll a and b can be recognised due to their relative positions and closeness to the correct Rf values.
D: Rf value: 0.30. Pigment: xanthophyll

2. There should be no effect on the Rf values but the amount of separation will be reduced.

11. Photosynthesis (page 15)

1. (a) Grana: Stacks of thylakoid membranes containing chlorophyll molecules. They are the site of the light dependent reactions of photosynthesis, which involve light energy capture via photosystems I and II.
   (b) Stroma: The liquid interior of the chloroplast in which the light independent phase takes place. This biochemical process involves carbon fixation (production of carbohydrate) via the Calvin cycle.

2. (a) Carbon dioxide: Comes from the air and provides carbon and oxygen as raw materials to produce glucose. Some oxygen contributes to the production of water.
   (b) Oxygen: Comes from CO_2 gas and water. The oxygen from the CO_2 is incorporated into glucose and H_2O. The oxygen from water is given off as free oxygen.
   (c) Hydrogen: Comes from H_2O from the soil. This hydrogen is incorporated into glucose and H_2O
   Note: Isotope studies show that the carbon and oxygen in the carbohydrate comes from CO_2, while the free oxygen comes from H_2O.

3. Triose phosphate is converted to glucose, which is fuel for respiration and used to construct disaccharides (e.g. sucrose), cellulose, or starch. Oxygen is used for aerobic respiration and water is recycled and even reused for photosynthesis.

12. Chloroplasts (page 16)

1. (a) Stroma   (d) Granum
   (b) Stroma lamellae (e) Thylakoid
   (c) Outer membrane   (f) Inner membrane

2. (a) Chlorophyll is found in the thylakoid membranes.
   (b) Chlorophyll is a membrane-bound pigment found in and around the photosystems embedded in the membranes. Light capture by chlorophyll is linked to electron transport in the light dependent reactions.

3. The internal membranes provide a large surface area for binding chlorophyll molecules and capturing light. Membranes are stacked in such a way that they do not shade each other.

4. Chlorophyll absorbs blue and red light but reflects green light, so leaves look green to the human eye.

13. Light Dependent Reactions (page 17)

1. NADP: Carries H_2 from the light dependent phase to the light independent reactions.

2. Chlorophyll molecules trap light energy and produce high energy electrons. These are used to make ATP and NADPH. The chlorophyll molecules also split water, releasing H^+ for use in the light independent reactions and liberating free O_2.

3. Light dependent (D) phase takes place in the grana (thylakoid membranes) of the chloroplast and requires light energy to proceed. The light dependent phase generates ATP and

reducing power in the form of NADPH. The electrons and hydrogen ions come from the splitting of water.

4. The ATP synthesis is coupled to electron transport. When the light strikes the chlorophyll molecules, high energy electrons are released by the chlorophyll molecules. The energy lost when the electrons are passed through a series of electron carriers is used to generate ATP from ADP and phosphate.

Note: ATP is generated (in photosynthesis and cellular respiration) by chemiosmosis. As the electron carriers pick up the electrons, protons (H^+) pass into the space inside the thylakoid, creating a high concentration of protons there. The protons return across the thylakoid membrane down a concentration gradient via the enzyme complex, ATP synthase, which synthesises ATP.

5. (a) Non-cyclic phosphorylation: Generation of ATP using light energy during photosynthesis. The electrons lost during this process are replaced by the splitting of water.
   (b) The term non-cyclic photophosphorylation is also (commonly) used because it indicates that the energy for the phosphorylation is coming from light.

6. (a) In cyclic photophosphorylation, the electrons lost from photosystem II are replaced by those from photosystem I rather than from the splitting of water. ATP is generated in this process, but not NADPH. **Note**: In the cell, both cyclic and non-cyclic photophosphorylation operate to different degrees to balance production of NADPH and ATP.
   (b) The non-cyclic path produces ATP and NADH in roughly equal quantities but the Calvin cycle uses more ATP than NADPH. The cyclic pathway of electron flow makes up the difference.

7.

	Non-cyclic phosphorylation	Cyclic phosphorylation
Photosystem	I and II	I
Energy carrier produced	NADPH, ATP	ATP
Photolysis of water	Yes	No
Production of oxygen	Yes	No

14. Light Independent Reactions (page 19)
1. (a) 6   (d) 12   (g) 2
   (b) 6   (e) 12   (h) 1
   (c) 12   (f) 6

2. RuBisCo catalyses the reaction that splits CO_2 and joins it with ribulose 1,5-bisphosphate. It fixes carbon from the atmosphere.

3. Triose phosphate (note that you may also see this referred to as glyceraldehyde-3-phosphate, GALP, G3P or PGAL)

4. $6CO_2 + 18ATP + 12 NADPH + 12H^+$
   $\rightarrow 1$ glucose $+18ADP + 18Pi + 12 NADP^+ + 6H_2O$

5. The light dependent reactions stop, therefore no NADPH or ATP is produced. At night, stomata also close, reducing levels of CO_2 (there will still be some CO_2 in the leaf as a waste product of respiration).

15. Experimental Investigation of Photosynthesis (page 20)
1. $DCPIP + 2H^+ + 2e^- \rightarrow DCPIPH_2$

2. Hill's experiment showed that water must be the source of the oxygen liberated in photosynthesis.

3. The reactions happen very quickly. By taking the sample only seconds apart, each step of the reaction can be worked out by recording the order of appearance of the reaction products.

16. Investigating Enzymes in Photosynthesis (page 21)
1. If light intensity affects the rate of dehydrogenase activity, then DCPIP will fade at a faster rate when exposed to a high light intensity than when exposed to a lower light intensity.

2.

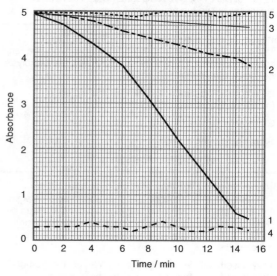

Enzyme activity in photosynthesis

3. (a) Tube 4 is a control to test if the DCPIP is responsible for the colour change.
   (b) Tube 5 is a control to test that the colour change is due to the leaf extract (not an unrelated reaction or light alone).

4. Tube 3 can only be exposed to the light for a short time to test that DCPIP does not fade in the dark (no reactions occurring).

5. The variation is due to natural variation of the absorbance reading (e.g minor variations in angle of tube etc).

6. Dehydrogenase activity (as an indirect measure of the rate of the light dependent reactions of photosynthesis) increases with an increase in light intensity.

17. The Fate of Triose Phosphate (page 22)
1. Two triose phosphate molecules are used to form a glucose molecule.

2. Glucose has three main fates: storage, building macromolecules, or production of usable energy (ATP).

3. In plants, glucose can be converted to (any one of): starch (energy storage in plastids) or cellulose (cell wall component). **Note**: Plants also produce fructan (energy storage).

4. Glucose is produced using a ^{13}C or ^{14}C. When the glucose is used to make other molecules, the C isotopes can be detected by the radioactivity or by density change of tissues or products into which the carbon has been incorporated.

18. Factors Affecting Photosynthesis (page 23)
1. (a) CO_2 concentration: Photosynthetic rate increases as the CO_2 concentration increases, and then levels off.
   (b) Light intensity: Photosynthetic rate increases rapidly as the light intensity increases and then levels off.
   (c) Temperature: Increased temperature increases the photosynthetic rate, but this effect is not marked at low concentrations of CO_2.

2. The photosynthetic rate is determined by the rate at which CO_2 enters the leaf. When this declines because of low atmospheric levels, so does photosynthetic rate.

3. (a) By changing only one factor at a time (temperature or CO_2 level) it is possible to assess the effects of each one.
   (b) CO_2 has the greatest effect of these two variables.
   (c) At low levels of CO_2, increase in temperature has little effect (the rate of CO_2 entry into the leaf is the greatest determinant of photosynthetic rate).

4. Glasshouses are controlled environments in which the levels

of light, humidity, temperature, and CO_2 can be optimised to maximise photosynthetic rate. In particular, CO_2 enrichment in an environment where transpiration losses are minimised enables maximum productivity.

5. Student's own experimental design. Possible hypothesis is that temperature will increase the rate of photosynthesis within limits (H_0 being no effect of temperature). The choice of design and plant will be up to the student but an easy one to choose is to measure the rate of oxygen (air bubble) production in a submerged aquatic macrophyte such as *Elodea*. The temperature can then be easily changed by heating or cooling the water. Things the student should make reference to and explain if necessary:

   - the control and how it was set up
   - how the dependent variable (biological response) is to be measured and how many measurements will be made
   - how the independent variable (temperature) is to be varied and the range of that variation
   - how other variables are kept constant and the value of these variables (e.g. light level)
   - how many plants at each treatment level

19. Investigating Photosynthetic Rate (page 24)

1. Missing figures for bubbles per minute are (in order of low light intensity to high light intensity): 0, 2, 3, 4, 6, 11, 11.67

2.

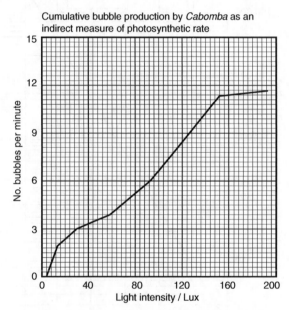

Cumulative bubble production by *Cabomba* as an indirect measure of photosynthetic rate

3. Photosynthetic rate increases with increasing light intensity. Although light intensity theoretically drops off at a constant rate, this may not practically occur due to shadows, variations in the equipment being used, or other light pollution. It is therefore better to measure the light intensity rather than infer light intensity from distance.

4. The gas was oxygen.

5. Instead of counting the bubbles (which could vary in volume) the gas could be collected and the volume produced measured. This could be done by displacement of water in a graduated cylinder or by using a photosynthometer.

20. Overcoming Limiting Factors in Photosynthesis (page 25)

1. CO_2 enrichment increases the rate of photosynthesis and so also the formation of dry plant matter (growth) and total yield (flowers or fruit).

2. Controlling the airflow ensures a homogeneous air temperature and an even distribution of carbon dioxide. This maximises yield because all plants receive optimum temperature gas concentrations for growth.

3. Temperature, carbon dioxide concentration, humidity, soil composition, air movement, and light intensity are some of the abiotic factors controlled in a greenhouse environment.

21. Chapter Review (page 26)
No model answer. Summary is the student's own.

22. KEY TERMS AND IDEAS: Did You Get It? (page 28)

1. absorption spectrum (H), alcoholic fermentation (E), Calvin cycle (I), cellular respiration (K), electron transport chain (N), glycolysis (A), grana (F), Krebs cycle (J), light dependent phase (G), link reaction (D), matrix (O), mitochondria (C), oxidative phosphorylation (B), pyruvate (L), ribulose bisphosphate (M).

2. (a) 2 ATP   (e) Electron transport chain (ETC)
   (b) 2 ATP   (f) Glucose
   (c) 34 ATP   (g) Carbon dioxide
   (d) Krebs cycle   (h) Water

3. (a) Water + carbon dioxide → glucose + oxygen
      $H_2O + CO_2 \rightarrow C_6H_{12}O_6 + O_2$
   (b) Photosynthesis takes place in the chloroplasts.

4.

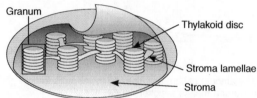

Granum
Thylakoid disc
Stroma lamellae
Stroma

23. Culturing Microorganisms (page 31)

1. (a) A selective growth medium is a growth medium that enhances the growth of certain microorganisms while discouraging the growth of others.
   (b) Selective media are an important tool when attempting to isolate particular groups of microorganisms from others, or to distinguish closely related microbes.
   (c) Selective media work by containing specific substances that are required for growth and metabolism by the microbes of interest while also containing substances (e.g. antibiotics) that stop the growth of unwanted microbes.

2. Use of aseptic technique ensures that only the microbes of interest are introduced to the culture and contaminants from the environment are excluded.

3. If the inoculation loop was not cooled the microbes would be killed before they could be transferred.

24. Dilution Plating (page 33)

1. 19 colonies X 100 000 = 1.9×10^6 cells per cm^3

2. (a) Viable count: The number of living cells in the culture (cells capable of reproducing).
   (b) In dilution plating, only viable cells will give rise to countable colonies. The calculated culture density will therefore refer to the number of viable cells.
   (c) Turbidimetry: An indirect method where culture turbidity is measured using absorbance on a colorimeter. The colorimeter is set at zero using the culture medium and subsequent absorbance readings above zero are taken as measures of microbial density. The culture density is determined from a standard calibration curve. **Note**: The technique provides no indication of viable cells, since most cells (except those that have sedimented out) will contribute to the absorbance reading.

© 2017 **BIOZONE** International
ISBN: 978-1-927309-28-5
Photocopying Prohibited

25. Investigating Bacterial Growth (page 34)

1. The precautions prevent the accidental introduction of the bacteria into the environment and prevent accidental infection.

2. (a) See graph below.

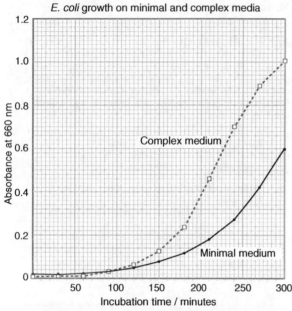

E. coli growth on minimal and complex media

(b) The amount of light absorbed by the sample (more light absorbed means a higher density of cells).
(c) The complex medium supported more rapid growth to a higher cell density relative to the minimal medium.

3. Use a standard calibration curve of bacterial density against absorbance or use dilution plating as per previous activity.

26. Strain Isolation (page 35)

1. Streak plating isolates individual colonies, making them easier to study and/or count.

2. Streak plating is based on the progressive reduction in the number of bacteria used to make each new streak. By the time the last streak is completed, the sample is so diluted that individual colonies may be isolated.

3. Petri dish lids are only partially removed to help prevent microbes in the air or on dust settling onto the agar and contaminating it.

4. (a) There would be well isolated colonies.
    (b) You could transfer the colonies to a selective medium that promoted growth of one species.

27. Isolating a Bacterial Species (page 36)

1. Colony 1 has a flat elevation profile, whereas colony 3 has a raised profile.

2. (a) Students could use aseptic technique to remove each colony type to a new plate with a selective growth medium that encouraged the growth of each particular species.
    (b) Once colony 3 was transferred, the colony should be allowed to grow and then a second round of streak plating performed to test that only the cells of colony 3 species were transferred.
    (c) Because colony 1 and 3 overlap, there is a risk that some cells of colony 1 would be transferred with colony 3.

3. The student's must not have used aseptic technique or their aseptic technique must have been inadequate and the plate has been contaminated by spores from the environment.

28. Microbial Growth Curve (page 36)

1. The initial lag is a result of there being little or no cell division occurring, hence no perceivable growth in cell number (the cells are increasing in size, but not dividing).

2. (a) Log phase
    (b) In a closed system, microbial growth will be limited by depletion of nutrient and build up of toxic waste products, so growth will slow.

3. Rate of cells dying exceeds growth rate (rate of cell division).

4. $\mu = 2.303 \times (7 - 3) \div 5 = 1.84$
    $g = (7 - 3) \div 0.301 = 13.3$ min

29. Plotting Microbial Growth (page 38)

1. Completed table below:

Min	No.	Min	No.	Min	No.
0	1	140	128	260	8 192
20	2	160	256	280	16 384
40	4	180	512	300	32 768
60	8	200	1024	320	65 536
80	16	220	2048	340	131 072
100	32	240	4096	360	262 144
120	64				

2. (a) 8   (b) 512   (c) 262 144

3.

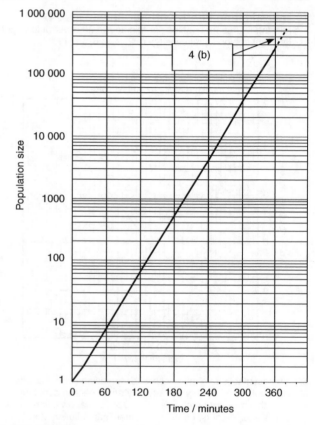

4 (b)

4. (a) 524 288
    (b) See graph above

5. With exponential growth, the numbers are very low initially, but increase quickly and very large numbers are involved. The log graph makes it feasible to plot the very small and very large numbers together in a reasonable space and in a way that is easy to read and interpret.

30. Bacterial Pathogens (page 39)

1. A pathogen is a disease-causing agent, such as a bacterium or virus.

2. Pathogenic bacteria can enter the body through natural body openings or through breaks in the skin surface. The tuberculosis bacterium, *Mycobacterium tuberculosis*, enters through the respiratory tract, spread through the air by coughing and sneezing. *Salmonella* and other gastrointestinal pathogens enter through the gastroinestinal tract where the toxins they produce cause the symptoms of food poisoning. Many sexually transmitted infections, e.g. gonorrhoea, enter

© 2017 **BIOZONE** International
ISBN: 978-1-927309-28-5
Photocopying Prohibited

through the urinogenital tract. *Staphylococcus aureus*, which causes a range of mild to serious skin infections, enters the body through breaks in the skin's surface.

3. (a) *Mycobacterium tuberculosis* invades the lung tissue. The bacilli are ingested by macrophages in the alveoli, where some can escape destruction and multiply. Tubercular nodules form, which may rupture creating cavities and scarring. The damage to the lung tissue is accompanied by coughing.
   (b) The pathogenic effect of Salmonella is a result of endotoxins released when cells die. The immune system cannot neutralise these toxins with antibodies, and their presence in the gastrointestinal tract damages intestinal cells, impairs fluid absorption, causes diarrhoea, and may result in toxic shock.
   (c) *Staphylococcus* exerts its pathogenic effect through the production of exotoxins, which are highly toxic and produce widespread effects on the host by destroying membranes, interfering with cellular metabolism, and causing inflammation.

4. Exotoxins are produced (primarily) by gram positive bacteria as part of their normal growth and metabolism whereas endotoxins (lipopolysaccharides) are released from gram negative bacteria as a result of cell lysis (when cells die).

5. (a) Exotoxins: *Staphylococcus* species.
   (b) Endotoxins: *Salmonella* species.

31. Antibiotics (page 41)
1. Antibiotics target the structures and metabolic pathways of bacteria. Viruses have a very different structure to bacteria, and no metabolic machinery of their own, so antibiotics are ineffective against them.

2. Bacteriostatic antibiotics prevent bacteria growing whereas bactericidal antibiotics kill the cells directly (cause cell lysis).

3. Bacteriostatic: chloramphenicol. The bacterial population remains the same over the length of the experiment. Bactericidal: ampicillin. The bacterial population decreases over the length of the experiment.

4. Penicillin interferes with the synthesis of the bacterial cell wall by inhibiting the enzyme that forms the peptidoglycan cross linkages and causes cell lysis (kills the cells and prevents bacterial populations increasing). Penicillins work on gram positive bacteria which have a cell wall largely of peptidoglycan. Tetracycline is bacteriostatic and inhibits bacterial growth. Because it inhibits protein synthesis it affects many different bacterial pathogens (it is broad spectrum).

5. (a) A
   (b) 3
   (c) This concentration in most effective as it produces the best result with the least amount of antibiotic used.

32. The Evolution of Antibiotic Resistance (page 43)
1. Resistance can become widespread as a result of:
   (a) Transfer of genetic material between bacteria (horizontal gene transmission).
   (b) Increasing resistance with each generation is a result of natural selection (vertical gene transmission). In this case, the antibiotic provides the selective environment.

2. (a) The genes for antibiotic resistance probably arose as a result of copying errors during DNA replication.
   (b) Antibiotic use is now widespread, providing a strong selective environment for proliferation of bacteria with genes for antibiotic-resistance.

3. (a) MDR TB cases have increased over the last decade (but there has been a decrease in Africa in the last few years).
   (b) MTB is becoming resistant to drugs commonly used to treat TB. This will make it harder to treat and eradicate the disease and more people will suffer complications or die.

33. The Implications of Antibiotic Resistance (page 44)
1. Antibiotic resistance allows bacteria to spread more easily between people. If no alternative antibiotics are available to treat the bacterial infection, more people will suffer medical

complications or die. Social impacts include an increasing strain on health providers, loss of income to infected individuals, and reduced productivity.

2. Rigorous basic hygiene practices (e.g. hand washing) and reporting have significantly reduced the transmission of MRSA in hospitals. The cases of MRSA developing can be reduced by ensuring that people are prescribed the correct course of antibiotics only when needed and that, once prescribed they complete the full course.

34. Fungi, Viruses, and Protozoan Pathogens (page 45)
1. A pathogen must spread from host to host and avoid a host's immune response.

2. If a host is killed too quickly, there is not enough time for it to be transmitted to new hosts and the pathogens spread (success) would be impaired.

3. Some outbreaks "burn out" quickly because they can cause death before they are able to be passed on. In cases of dispersed populations, the disease may cause a few deaths then disappear due to lack of hosts.

35. Stem Rust Fungus (page 46)
1. Stem rust disease infects a large number of cereal crops important as staples in the human diet. Yield losses therefore represent a threat to food security.

2. *P. graminis* spreads by spores and the life cycle involves barberry and cereal plant hosts. Spores from an infected plant land on a new plant and germinate, penetrating the leaf or stalk and producing mycelium that utilises the plant's nutrients and the sugars it produces (i.e. it is a parasite).

3. *P. graminis* weakens the plant stem and causes the plants to collapse. Reduced nutrition leads to smaller deformed grains (fruits) and a drop in grain yield (hence large economic losses). Disruption of stomatal function disrupts control of transpiration and can lead to poor resistance to dry conditions (increased desiccation, increased crop losses, and increased costs of irrigation).

36. The Influenza Virus (page 47)
1. The flu virus is easily spread by coughing and sneezing and survives outside the body for up to 24 hours so can be transmitted indirectly via contaminated surfaces such as hands, door handles, keyboards etc.

2. *Influenzavirus* binds to receptors on the host's cell surface and is taken into the cell by endocytosis. It then takes over the cell's metabolic machinery to transcribe the viral genetic material and manufacture new viral particles. Assembled viral particles bud off the host cell to infect new cells.

3. *Influenzavirus* has a high mutation rate and small changes to the protein coat happen continually so that vaccines must be adjusted annually to maintain effectiveness. Previously vaccinated people will not have immunity to new strains. In addition, antigenic shifts, in which two or more viral strains combine, produce new virulent strains for which new vaccines must be developed.

37. Malaria (page 48)
1. A mosquito carrying the parasite bites a human. The parasite is injected along with the saliva.

2. (a) The parasite travels in the blood to the liver. They grow and multiply first in the liver cells and then in the red blood cells. Broods of parasites multiply in the red blood cells, and are released in waves to reinfect more cells.
   (b) Infection by *Plasmodium* and replication of the parasite within the causes waves of fever and chills as new red blood cells are infected. While in the liver, the parasite is undetected by the immune system, which only responds when the parasites are released from lysed cells.
   (c) Adhesive proteins on the cell surfaces advantage the parasite because it removes the infected cells from circulation, preventing them being transported to the spleen and destroyed. The sticky cells block small blood vessels and cause circulation problems and the more

© 2017 **BIOZONE** International
ISBN: 978-1-927309-28-5
Photocopying Prohibited

severe symptoms, including convulsions and coma.

38. Malaria is Endemic in Some Countries (page 49)

1. *Plasmodium* has a complex life cycle with two hosts, so the vector must be controlled as well as the parasite itself. Both vectors and parasites show resistance to control measures so transmission remains high in malarial regions.

2. Poor rural populations do not have the resources to obtain simple protection measures such as mosquito nets. Poorer countries also lack the financial resources to provide medicine and trained staff to control and treat malaria. Malaria transmission is therefore higher and treatment less effective in these countries.

3. (a) **Note**: Restricted use of DDT for malaria control is allowed under a public health exemption.

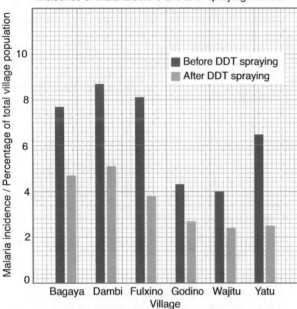

Incidence of malaria before and after spraying with DDT

(b) Yes, insecticide spraying was an effective preventative measure against malaria because it reduced the incidence (occurrence of new cases) by 38%- >60%.
(c) If DDT resistance became widespread, the spray control measures would cease to have any effect.

4. Malaria affects relatively more low income populations and economically more disadvantaged countries (which do not have the resources to prevent or treat the disease). New drugs and insecticides are expensive to develop and the populations that need them the most are unlikely to be able to afford them. Companies developing new products for prevention and treatment should be ethically obliged to make them affordable to these populations.

39. The Body's Defences (page 51)

1. **Specific resistance** refers to defence against identified pathogens. It involves a range of specific responses to the pathogen (antibody production and cell-mediated immunity). **Non-specific resistance** refers to defence against any type of pathogen. It takes the form of physical and chemical barriers against infection, as well as phagocytosis and inflammation.

2. The skin provides a physical barrier to prevent entry of pathogens. Skin secretions (serum and sweat) contain antimicrobial chemicals which inhibit microbial growth.

3. A three tiered (hierarchical) system of defence provides a series of back-ups in case a pathogen breaches earlier barriers. Most microbes are excluded by the first line of defence, but those that penetrate the skin will usually be destroyed by white blood cells and the chemicals associated with inflammation. Failing this, the body will mount a targeted

specific defence against the identified pathogen still remaining.

4. (a) The main type of WBCs present are neutrophils.
(b) The high number of neutrophils and elevated WBC count indicates the person has an infection.
(c) Blood smear B is normal.
(d) The total WBC count is within the normal range, and there are no elevated levels of any particular WBC.

40. The Innate Immune Response (page 53)

1. (a) Macrophages use amoeboid movements to hunt and destroy pathogens.
(b) Neutrophils contain toxic substances that kill or inhibit the growth of pathogens. Neutrophils also release cytokines which amplify the immune response and recruit other cells to the infection site.
(c) Dendritic cells act as messengers between the innate and adaptive immune system by presenting antigens on their surfaces so that T cells can recognise them.

2. The complement system has three main roles in immunity. It comprises proteins that have roles in phagocytosis, attracting macrophages and neutrophils to the infection site, and rupturing the membranes of foreign cells.

3. (a) Increased diameter and permeability of blood vessels. Role: Increases blood flow and delivery of leucocytes to the area. Helps remove destroyed microbes or their toxins. Lets defensive substances leak into the tissue spaces.
(b) Phagocyte migration and phagocytosis. Role: To directly attack and destroy microbes and foreign substances.
(c) Tissue repair. Role: Replaces damaged cells and tissues, restoring the integrity of the area.

4. Mast cells contain histamine, a chemical involved in both inflammation and allergic reactions. Histamine causes blood vessels to become leaky. This allows phagocytes to reach the site of infection.

5. Pus (accumulated debris of infection including damaged tissue, dead phagocytes, and fluid) accumulates at the site of infection where the defence process is most active.

41. Phagocytes and Phagocytosis (page 55)

1. Neutrophils, dendritic cells, macrophages. Eosinophils also show some phagocytosis.

2. Opsonins coat foreign material, marking it as a target for phagocytosis. The opsonins bind to the phagocyte receptors, triggering engulfment of the foreign material by phagocytes.

3. Microbes may be able to produce toxins that kill phagocytes directly. Others can enter the phagocytes, completing filling them and preventing them functioning or remaining dormant and resuming activity later.

42. Processing Antigens (page 56)

1. Antigen processing prepares and displays antigens for presentation to the T-cells of the immune system.

2. MHC receptors with no foreign antigen bound signal to the T cells that the cell is healthy and can be ignored.

3. MHC I receptors display antigenic peptides of intracellular parasites such as viruses. MHC II receptors display antigenic peptides originating from the outside of the cell.

43. The Lymphatic System (page 57)

1. The lymphatic system collects fluid leaked from the blood vessels and returns it to the heart. This fluid, called lymph, circulates defensive white blood cells between the lymphoid organs and other tissues of the body.

2. (a) Lymph nodes are the sites of lymphocyte activation (where antigens are presented to lymphocytes) and proliferation. From the lymph nodes, the activated lymphocytes can enter the general circulation.
(b) The lymph nodes swell because large numbers of lymphocytes are being produced there.

© 2017 **BIOZONE** International
ISBN: 978-1-927309-28-5
Photocopying Prohibited

44. The Adaptive Immune System (page 58)

1. Bone marrow and fetal liver

2. (a) Bone marrow   (b) Thymus gland

3. (a) **Humoral immune system**: Production of antibodies against specific antigens. The antibodies disable circulating antigens.
   (b) **Cell-mediated immune system**: Involves the T cells, which destroy pathogens or their toxins by direct contact or by producing substances that regulate the activity of other immune system cells.

4. The presence of an antigen results in the proliferation of specific types of B- and T-cell to target that antigen. First, the antigen is engulfed by a phagocytic dendritic cell, which then presents the antigen on its surface and secretes cytokines. These processes activate T helper cells leading to the proliferation of T cell types and the production of antibody-producing B cells.

5. Dendritic cells act as messengers by processing antigens and presenting them to T cells so that specific antigens can be recognised and targeted.

6. (a) T helper cells: Activate T killer cells and other T helper cells. Also needed for B cell activation.
   (b) T cytotoxic cells: Destroy target cells on contact (by binding and lysing cells).

45. Clonal Selection (page 60)

1. Millions of B-cells form during development. Each B-cell recognises one antigen only and produces antibodies against it. A pathogen will trigger a response in the B-cell that is specific for it, resulting in proliferation of that B-cell. This is called clonal selection (the antigen selects the B-cell clone that will proliferate).

2. (a) Plasma cells secrete antibodies against antigens (very rapid rate of antibody production).
   (b) The antibodies match the specific antigenic receptors on the B cell. Millions of antibodies are produced and are able to float through the blood and bind corresponding antigens, multiplying the immune response.

3. (a) Immunological memory: The result of the differentiation of B cells after the first exposure to an antigen. Those B cells that differentiate into long lived memory cells are present to react quickly and vigorously in the event of a second infection.
   (b) Memory cells respond quickly because they retain an antigenic memory. This means they can rapidly differentiate into antibody-producing plasma cells if they encounter the same antigen again.

46. Antibodies (page 61)

1. Antibodies consist of two heavy (long) peptide chains each attached to a light (short) peptide chain, commonly forming a Y configuration. The variable region at the ends of the heavy and light chains form the antigen binding sites.

2. (a) Agglutinins bind antigens together inactivating them and stopping them from infecting or damaging cells.
   (b) Antitoxins bind and neutralise toxins, stopping them from damaging cells.
   (c) Opsonins act as tags that antibodies recognise, enhancing the ability of phagocytes to engulf and destroy antigens.

47. Acquired Immunity (page 62)

1. (a) Immunity as a result of antibodies transferred from one person to another. In this case, the recipient does not make the antibodies themselves.
   (b) Naturally acquired passive immunity arises as a result of antibodies passing from the mother to the fetus/infant via the placenta/breast milk. Artificially acquired passive immunity arises as a result of injection with immune serums e.g. in antivenoms.

2. (a) Newborns need to be supplied with maternal antibodies because they have not yet had exposure to the everyday microbes in their environment and must be born with operational defence mechanisms.
   (b) The antibody supply is ideally supplemented with antibodies in breast milk because it takes time for the infant's immune system to become fully functional. **Note**: During this time, the supply of antibodies received during pregnancy will decline.
   (c) Yes. Breast feeding will provide the infant with a naturally acquired passive immunity to help protect it against infections while its immune system develops. Without this acquisition, the infant is more vulnerable to everyday infections against which you already have immunity but he/she does not.

3. (a) Immunity as a result of the immune response caused by exposure to a microbe or its toxins.
   (b) Naturally acquired active immunity arises as a result of exposure to an antigen such as a pathogen, e.g. natural immunity to chickenpox. Artificially acquired active immunity arises as a result of vaccination, e.g. any childhood disease for which vaccinations are given: diphtheria, measles, mumps, polio etc.

4. (a) The primary response is of a smaller magnitude than the secondary response. The primary response takes longer to develop and is over more quickly than the secondary response, which is rapid and long lasting.
   (b) The immune system has already been prepared to respond to the antigen by the first exposure to it. When exposed to the same antigen again, it can respond quickly with rapid production of antibodies.

48. Vaccines and Vaccination (page 64)

1. (a) A vaccine is a preparation of a harmless foreign antigen deliberately introduced into the body to prepare the immune system to resist that pathogen.
   (b) Vaccinations are needed for protection against common, dangerous, or contagious diseases. They are needed in childhood to protect against life threatening common childhood diseases, to protect against infection after injury (e.g. tetanus), and when travelling to countries with a high incidence of certain diseases (e.g. yellow fever).

2. Attenuated viruses are more effective in the long term because they tend to replicate in the body, and the original dose therefore increases over time. This doesn't happen with inactivated viruses, which contain only antigenic fragments. **Note**: Live vaccines are derived from viruses with mutations accumulated over time in a laboratory culture, so there is always a risk that they will back-mutate to a virulent form.

3. (a) Herd immunity refers to the protection that unimmunised people have against a circulating disease by virtue of the fact that most of the population are immunised.
   (b) Once the population contains a high proportion of non-vaccinated people, herd immunity is lost and a circulating disease can spread very rapidly through the community.

4. Herd immunity provides protection to people who cannot be vaccinated, e.g. cancer patients, the very young, or people with immune system disorders. Herd immunity reduces the number of potential carriers of a disease and so reduces the chance that an unvaccinated person will come into contact with the disease.

49. Vaccines Can Eliminate Infectious Disease (page 66)

1. (a) Introduction of the vaccine resulted in a sharp decrease in whooping cough notifications. Rates continued to drop (with seasonal fluctuations) until the late 1970s when vaccination rates fell and cases increased again.
   (b) Whole agent vaccines, which provided protection against many pertussis strains, are no longer used. The newer acellular vaccines contains only five antigens and provides much less resistance to infection. In addition, new strains are continually evolving and vaccinated adults are now contracting the disease, suggesting the vaccination does not provide lifelong protection.

2. A pregnant woman who has been vaccinated will pass antibodies to the pathogen to her fetus across the placenta

so the child, when born, will have passive immunity, which will protect them until they are old enough to be vaccinated.

50. Questions about Vaccines (page 67)
1. (a) The rate decreases from over 90% to ~80% before beginning to rise again around 2004-2005.
   (b) The drop in vaccination rates coincided with an increase in measles cases 2001-2004, but the pattern is inconsistent after 2005, with cases increasing, falling, and then increasing despite a recovery in vaccination rates.

51. Chapter Review (page 68)
No model answer. Summary is the student's own.

52. KEY TERMS AND IDEAS: Did You Get It? (page 70)
1. aseptic technique (P), active immunity (E), antibodies (M), antigen (H), B cells (N), clonal selection (L), exotoxin (K), immunity (J), lag phase (C), passive immunity (G), phagocytes (O), stationary phase (B), specific immune response (I), streak plating (A), T cells (F), vaccination (D).

2. (a) Artificially acquired immunity
   (b) First vaccination
   (c) Second vaccination
   (d) The first vaccination causes a small primary response in which antibodies and memory cells are produced. The secondary response is much larger because the body has already produced memory cells that quickly divide into antibody producing cells when the antigen is encountered a second time.

3. (a) A and C
   (b) B and E
   (c) They are gram positive (sensitive to penicillin).

4. (a) Bactericidal kills, e.g. penicillin against gram positive
   (b) Bacteriostatic inhibits, e.g. tetracycline (broad spectrum)

53. Genomes (page 73)
1. (a) Genome: All the genetic material in one haploid set of chromosomes.
   (b) Genes: Sections of DNA that code for proteins.
   (c) Allele: A version of a gene. Different alleles produce slightly different versions of a protein.

2. In general, the genome size and gene number increase from viruses to bacteria to eukaryotes,

3. Viruses and bacteria are haploid, with only one chromosome (excluding plasmids). Therefore they can only have one allele per gene. Because eukaryotes are diploid (two sets of chromosomes) they can have two different alleles for a gene. **Note**: some eukaryotes, especially plants and fish, can have more than two chromosome sets, e.g. triploid.

54. PCR and Modern Genetics (page 74)
1. To produce large quantities of 'cloned' DNA from very small samples. Large quantities are needed for effective analysis. Very small quantities are often unusable.

2. Detail not necessarily required in the answer is in parentheses. A double stranded DNA is heated (to 98°C for 5 min), causing the two strands to separate. Primers, free nucleotides, and DNA polymerase are added to the sample. The sample is then cooled (to 60°C for a few minutes), and the primers anneal to the DNA strands. The sample is incubated and complementary strands are created (by the DNA polymerase) using each strand of the DNA sample as a template. The process is repeated about 25 times, each time the number of templates doubles over the previous cycle.

3. (a) Forensic samples taken at the scene of a crime (e.g. hair, blood, semen).
   (b) Samples from extinct organisms, e.g. the remains of organisms mummified or preserved in ice, amber, or tar, or archaeological samples (early human remains).

4. This exercise can be done on a calculator by pressing the 1 button (for the original sample) and then multiplying by 2

repeatedly (to simulate each cycle).
   (a) 1024
   (b) 33 554 432 (33.5 million)

5. (a) It would be amplified along with the intended DNA sample, contaminating the sample and rendering it unusable.
   (b) Sources of contamination (any two of):
   Dirty equipment (equipment that has DNA molecules left on it from previous treatments).
   DNA from the technician (dandruff from the technician is a major source of contamination!)
   Spores, viruses and bacteria in the air.
   (c) Precautions to avoid contamination (any two of):
   Using disposable equipment (pipette tips, gloves).
   Wearing a **head cover** (disposable cap).
   Use of **sterile procedures**.
   Use of **plastic disposable tubes with caps** that seal the contents from air contamination.

55. Applications of Gene Sequencing (page 76)
1. DNA sequencing determines the order of bases in DNA so it can be used to predict the mRNA sequence and therefore the protein product of any gene.

2. The DNA sequence data of individuals affected or unaffected by a disease can be compared and computer analysed to identify genotypes with DNA changes (mutations). These changes can be linked to the occurrence of the disease. **Note**: Complex genomic variations can be analysed this way and links to disease established sing statistical methods.

56. Gene Sequencing and Medicine (page 77)
1. After a genome is sequenced, genes are identified, cross referenced with other known similar genes, and their functions investigated. Existing drugs targeting similar genes or gene products can be identified and their effectiveness against the newly identified genes and their products tested. Once a gene product is known, it can be synthesised and tested on a model organism so that new vaccines or drugs can be developed to target the newly identified genes.

2. The completion of the *P. falciparum* genome has enabled the identification of specific gene loci that encode antigens. These can be used to develop a vaccine against malaria (antigenic material is the basis of vaccination). However, few of the loci are shared by all *Plasmodium* species, so a single vaccine against all species is unlikely.

57. DNA Profiling (page 78)
1. STRs (microsatellites) are non-coding nucleotide sequences (2-6 base pairs long) that repeat themselves many times over (repeats of up to 100X). The human genome has numerous different STRs; equivalent sequences in different people vary considerably in the numbers of the repeating unit. This property can be used to identify the natural variation found in every person's DNA since every person will have a different combination of STRs of different repeat length, i.e. their own specific genetic profile.

2. (a) Gel electrophoresis: Used to separate the DNA fragments (STRs) according to size to create the fingerprint (profile).
   (b) PCR: Used to make many copies of the STRs. Only the STR sites are amplified by PCR because the primers used to initiate the PCR are very specific.

3. (a) Extract the DNA from sample. Treat the tissue with chemicals and enzymes to extract the DNA, which is then separated and purified.
   (b) Amplify the microsatellite using PCR. Primers are used to make large quantities of the STR.
   (c) Run the fragments through a gel to separate them. The resulting pattern represents the STR sizes for that individual (different from that of other people).

4. To ensure that the number of STR sites, when compared, will produce a profile that is effectively unique (different from just about every other individual). It provides a high degree of statistical confidence when a match occurs.

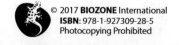

58. Forensic Applications of DNA Profiling (page 80)

1. Profiles of everyone involved must be completed to compare their DNA to any DNA found at the scene and therefore eliminate (or implicate) them as suspects.

2. The alleged offender is not guilty. The alleged offender's DNA profile does not appear in the DNA collected at the crime scene nor does it appear in the DNA database. Profile E's DNA is found at the scene.

3. (a) 0.0294
   (b) 0.3446
   (c) $2pq = 2 \times 0.0294 \times 0.3446 = 0.0203$

4. 14-10, 14-11, 15-10, 15-11

5. (a) No
   (b) The man cannot be the biological father because there are two mismatches in the profiles. The child does not show any matches with STR D19S433 and D2S441.

6. (a) Each whale species has a distinct DNA profile. Profiling the whale meat therefore reveals the types of whales they meat came from.
   (b) Individual whales also have their own DNA profile. Profiling the whale meat from each species reveals how many whales of that species were killed (by simply counting the number of different profiles.

59. Gene Expression Overview (page 82)

1. Tight regulation of gene expression ensures that proteins, which are energetically expensive to produce, are only produced when needed and in the quantities required.

2. Proteins can be modified after translation to enable them to take up their functional role.

3. (a) Exons: DNA sequences that are expressed into protein.
   (b) Introns: DNA sequences not expressed into protein.

60. Transcription factors Control Gene Expression (page 83)

1. (a) The promoter is the DNA sequence where transcription factors and RNA polymerase bind and where RNAP starts transcription.
   (b) The terminator sequence is a nucleotide sequence at the end of a protein coding region that functions to stop transcription.
   (c) The transcription start signal indicates where RNA polymerase will begin transcribing the DNA into mRNA.
   (d) The AUG code is where ribosomes will start translation of the mRNA code to produce a polypeptide chain.
   (e) UAA, UAG, and UGA are stop codons. They indicate where the ribosomes should stop translation and dissociate from the mRNA.

2. (a) The exons are spliced together to from the mature mRNA.
   (b) The introns are removed from the primary transcript.
   (c) The 5' and 3' UTR regions remain with the mRNA to be translated. **Note**: UTR have regulatory functions, e.g. for the safe export of the mRNA from the nucleus).

3. Transcribed but untranslated regions have a role regulating the expression of the gene or export of the mRNA from the nucleus.

4. (a) A transcription factor is a protein with a role in creating an initiation complex for RNAP binding and transcription.
   (b) Regulatory genes.
   (c) Transcription factors bind to distinct regions of the DNA (e.g. the promoter) and act as a guide to indicate where RNA polymerase should start transcription.

5. (a) The DNA sequence does not change between species (with evolution). The same sequence is present in the same position in all species.
   (b) Untranslated regions contain regulatory information. This information must be important in the development of any cell and any mutations in it would have negative effects on the cell's development. Therefore these regions are conserved (remain unchanged) by natural selection.

61. mRNA Processing (page 85)

1. The cap protects the mRNA from degradation. The tail aids export, translation, and stability.

2. (a) Introns are removed from the primary transcript.
   (b) Introns may be processed to produce regulatory elements.

3. Primary mRNA can be spliced and combined in many different ways to produce many protein variants. Proteins are also modified after translation.

4. Each gene produces 40 proteins on average
   (1 000 000 ÷ 25 000).

62. DNA Packaging and Transcription (page 86)

1. (a) Histones package the DNA in an orderly way (like coiling thread around a spool), enabling it to fit into the nucleus. The extent of packing also regulates gene expression.
   (b) Euchromatin is loosely packaged DNA (available for transcription).
   (c) Heterochromatin is tightly packaged DNA (unavailable for transcription)
   (d) Epigenetic factors are changes to the DNA , such as methylation, which do not alter the nucleotide sequence.

2. (a) DNA methylation generally causes the chromatin to bind more tightly together and suppresses gene expression.
   (b) Histone acetylation removes the positive charge on the histones, decreasing their interaction with the DNA so the DNA becomes looser and the genes become available for transcription.
   (c) Histone methylation generally (but not always) causes chromatin to be more tightly packed and reduces gene expression (although it can depend on which amino acids in the histones are methylated).

63. The Effect of DNA Methylation (page 87)

1. (a) Removing epigenetic markers (resetting) prevents the developmental potential of cells from being restricted. The cells begin development with a 'clean slate'.
   (b) Some markers escape resetting and are inherited. The past environment influences (e.g. of the parent) can therefore be tracked through the next generation. **Note**: This is thought to account for the inter-generational effects of factors such as famine.

2. Methylation is an important mechanism controlling the activation and inactivation of genes and so it directs the differentiation of all the cells and tissues of the body.

3. The embryo is also exposed to any environment the mother is exposed to. Chemicals ingested or absorbed by the mother can make their way through the blood and cross the placenta to the embryo. These chemicals can then affect the developing embryo by affecting gene expression.

64. Non-Coding RNA Can Silence Gene Expression (page 88)

1. siRNA is formed from exogenous dsRNA while miRNA is formed from hairpin loops of non-protein-coding RNA copied from endogenous DNA.

2. RNAi regulates gene expression by cleaving mRNA molecules, thus rendering them inactive. In this way proteins that would be coded for by genes are not expressed as their protein product is not made.

3. MicroRNAs are involved in silencing genes and regulating gene expression. If microRNAs are under-expressed there will be poor/insufficient regulation of cells proliferating out of control (tumour cells).

65. What Are Stem Cells? (page 89)

1. (a) Potency - ability to differentiate into other cell types.
   (b) Self renewal - ability to maintain an unspecialised state.

2. The differentiation of cells into specialised types is the result of specific patterns of gene expression and is controlled by transcription factors in response to cues (e.g. from hormones) during development. **Note** there are several levels of regulation here (see activity 59): Transcription

factors, which transcribe the genes and so ultimately regulate development, can only access the DNA when it is unpacked (as euchromatin), which is regulated by epigenetic factors such as methylation.

3. Stem cells differentiate to give rise to all the cell types of the multicellular organism. The zygote is totipotent and can differentiate into any cell type, including extra-embryonic cells. As development proceeds, the cells become pluripotent. They can give rise to most cell types, but not extra-embryonic cells, and are important in the early development of tissues and organs. Throughout life, multipotent adult stem cells maintain these tissues and organs and are committed to produce the different cell types related to the tissue of origin.

4. (a) Pluripotent stem cells are naturally found in the inner mass of the blastocyst and can give rise to any cells of the body (except extra-embryonic cells). iPSC are induced from somatic cells by the insertion of specific genes and give rise to unipotent stem cells which give rise only to one specific cell type.
   (b) The insertion of genes, known as reprogramming factors, Oct, Sox2, cMyc, and Klf4 induce an individual's somatic cells to revert to a more embryonic state (forming iPSC).
   (c) Induced pluripotent stem cells form unipotent stem cells which give rise to a specific cell type.

5. (a) In general, efficiency of conversion to iPSC is very low.
   (b) Some of the reprogramming factors used to form iPSC are proto-oncogenes and are implicated in cancer.

66. Epigenetic Factors Regulate Cell Differentiation (page 91)

1. As a cell progresses along a path of differentiation, genes are silenced or activated in different sequences by methylation or demethylation respectively (when methylated, transcription factors cannot access the gene and it cannot be transcribed). Demethyation allows a cell to progress to the next stage in its differentiation. By switching genes off and on in certain sequences, the cell is directed to follow a particular path towards becoming specialised into a certain cell type.

2. Disorders in epigenetic regulation can lead to a loss of silencing so that progenitor cells are not switched off appropriately and certain differentiated cell types continue to proliferate unchecked.

67. Stem Cells and the Treatment of Disease (page 92)

1. The stem cells from the donor may not be immunologically compatible and may be rejected by the recipient's immune system.

2. If stem cells carrying a defective gene are placed into the patient, there will be no benefit. The disease will not be corrected because the stem cells carry the same genetic defect. The gene must be corrected.

3. If the disease is the result of a genetic defect, the defective gene will also be present in the umbilical cord blood. If the genetic defect is uncorrected, the treatment will not be effective.

4. (a) Type 1 diabetes results from the body's immune system destroying the insulin-producing cells of the pancreas so that no insulin is produced and, as a consequence, the cells cannot take up glucose.
   (b) Stem cells taken from donors who do not have diabetes are induced to develop into insulin producing cells. They are then transplanted into the patient.

5. The ethical issues associated with stem cell therapies vary depending on whether the therapies involve ESC or ASC. ESC research is more fraught with potential ethical problems because it involves the creation and destruction of embryos, even though ESC therapies are potentially more useful because the cells are pluripotent. This aspect of ESC therapy raises issues such as the 'rights' of the embryo as a potentially human life, and the value of an existing life against the value of a 'potential' life. ESC has still not produced any viable treatments but ASC therapy has and its uses are less controversial because it does not involve the creation and

destruction of embryos.

68. Making Recombinant DNA (page 94)

1. Restriction enzymes are used to cut DNA into lengths or to isolate genes by cutting at specific recognition sites.

2. Sticky end fragments have exposed nucleotide bases at each end, whereas blunt end fragments have no exposed nucleotide bases. Sticky ends are joined via the complementary base pairing of the exposed bases.

3. Having many different kinds of restriction enzymes allows DNA to be cut at many different recognition sites and so produce a variety of sticky or blunt ends. This allows for a better ability to isolate and join different regions of the DNA.

4. (a) The two single-stranded DNA molecules are recombined into a double-stranded molecule. This is achieved by H-bonding between complementary bases.
   (b) DNA ligase joins two adjacent pieces of DNA by linking nucleotides in the sticky ends.

5. Ligation joins together DNA molecules, while restriction digestion (by restriction enzymes) cuts them up.

6. With a few exceptions, all organisms on Earth use the same DNA code to store information and the same cellular machinery to read the information and express it. Any DNA from any organism can therefore be read and expressed by the cellular machinery of any other organism into which the DNA is spliced.

69. Transgenic Organisms (page 96)

1. Transgenesis is the insertion of DNA (a gene) from one species of organism into another so that the gene's protein product is expressed in the second species. **Note**: For transgenesis to be successful, the gene must be transmitted to subsequent offspring.

2. Applications of transgenesis include (one of):
   – Modification of crop plants to alter their nutritional profile, environmental tolerance, or resistance to disease, pests, or herbicides.
   – Producing animals with specific genetic defects for medical or veterinary research so that disease processes can be studied and effective treatments can be developed.
   – Livestock improvement for characteristics such as wool or meat quality and quantity, and milk yield and nutritional profile.
   – Animal biofactories including the production of livestock that secrete therapeutic proteins in milk, or bacteria that produce valuable human proteins such as human insulin and factor VIII.

70. Vectors for Transgenesis (page 97)

1. (a) Viruses are good vectors because they are adapted to gain entry into a host's cells and integrate their DNA into that of the host.
   (b) Viral vectors can cause problems because (two of):
   • The host can develop a strong immune response to the viral infection. In patients disadvantaged (immune suppressed) by their disorder, this could severely undermine their health.
   • Viruses may not survive if attacked by the host's immune system.
   • Only short sequences of DNA can be carried by the virus.
   • The genes may integrate randomly into chromosomes and disrupt the functioning of normal genes.

2. Plasmids are used for:
   • Producing recombinant DNA for production of transgenic bacteria (or subsequent insertion into plants to produce genetically modified plant material).
   • Carrying new DNA into a cell for gene therapy.

71. Plasmids and Gene Cloning (page 98)

1. The human gene is prepared by removal of introns and promoter and terminator sequences added. At the same time, an appropriate vector (e.g. plasmid) is isolated. Both the gene and plasmid are treated with the same restriction enzyme

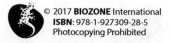

© 2017 **BIOZONE** International
ISBN: 978-1-927309-28-5
Photocopying Prohibited

(RE) to produce identical sticky ends. The RE used interrupts an antibiotic gene so that transformed cells can later be recognised. The DNA fragments are mixed in the presence of DNA ligase and anneal (DNA ligation). This produces a recombinant plasmid containing the human gene.

2. (a) Replica plating is used to identify colonies of bacteria that contain the recombinant plasmid (transformed cells).
   (b) Replating to the master media is a check to ensure that the transfer was successful (all should grow).
   (c) Colonies containing the human gene (which interrupts the tetracycline resistance gene) will grow on the ampicillin plate but not on the tetracycline plate. They can be identified on the original plate by their position because the spatial arrangement of colonies is maintained throughout the transfers.
   (d) The colony arose from a cell that did not take up the plasmid.

3. A *gfp* marker is preferable over antibiotic resistance genes because antibiotic resistance genes encourage the undesirable spread of antibiotic resistance through bacterial populations. Apart from this, a *gfp* marker system is much simpler, as the marked colonies can be quickly identified by fluorescence under UV light.

---

72. Determine Gene Function with Knockout Mice (page 100)

1. (a) Gene function could be studied using mutations that produced genes that were non-functional.
   (b) Mutations are random. This makes it difficult to identify which gene has the mutation and to reproduce the mutation. Even the use of mutagens will not always produce the same mutation. In addition, some genes may be highly conserved and therefore not mutate often.

2. (a) The non-functional gene is produced *in vitro* (in the laboratory).
   (b) The non-functional gene is introduced into the ESC by a vector. Those that take up the non-functional gene are injected into the blastocyst by microinjection.
   (c) Only some cells in the first generation mice will have the non-functional gene because these are the cells that are descended from the ESC injected into the early blastocyst.
   (d) The first generation of mice are chimaeras (some cells have the non-functional gene). These are cross-bred to produce second generation mice, which are heterozygous. These heterozygous mice are cross-bred to produce third generation homozygous mice.

3. Gene knockout is a technique used in mice to determine the effect of genes that mice and humans have in common. The knockouts (and there are several thousand strains) provide models for human diseases and behaviours, e.g. obesity, cancers, and sickle cell disease.

4. Gene knockouts, while useful, do not always replicate the effect of gene dysfunction in humans (e.g. p53 knockouts in mice produce tumours in different tissues to p53 mutations in humans). In addition, only a small proportion of knockouts are viable, so studying conditions of interest can be difficult.

---

73. A Model Transgenic: Engineering Human Insulin (page 102)

1. (a)-(c) in any order:
   - High cost (extraction from tissue is expensive).
   - Non-human insulin is different enough from human insulin to cause side effects.
   - The extraction methods did not produce pure insulin so the insulin was often contaminated.

2. Using recombinant DNA technology to produce human insulin provides a way to produce a low cost, reliable supply for consumer use. The insulin protein is free of contaminants and, because it is a human protein, the side effects of its use are minimised.

3. The insulin is synthesised as two (A and B) nucleotide sequences (corresponding to the two polypeptide chains) because a single sequence is too large to be inserted into the

bacterial plasmid. Two shorter sequences are small enough to be inserted (separately) into bacterial plasmids.

4. The β-galactosidase gene in *E.coli* has a promoter region so the synthetic genes must be tied to that gene in order to be transcribed.

5. (a) Insertion of the gene: The yeast plasmid is larger and can accommodate the entire synthetic nucleotide sequence for the A and B chains as one uninterrupted sequence.
   (b) Secretion and purification: Yeast, a eukaryote, has secretory pathways that are more similar to humans than those of a prokaryote and the β-galactosidase promoter is not required so secretion of the precursor insulin molecules is less problematic. Purification is simplified because removal of β-galactosidase is not required and the separate protein chains do not need to be joined.

---

74. Genetic Modification of Soybeans (page 104)

1. (a) Oleic acid, linoleic acid, palmitic acid, and stearic acid.
   (b) Linoleic acid.
   (c) Fatty acid dehydrogenase which converts oleic acid to the easily oxidised linoleic acid.
   (d) Hydrogenation is needed to artificially reduce the linoleic acid content. Increasing the oleic acid reduces the amount of linoleic acid, therefore reduces the oxidation, and so reduces the need for hydrogenation.

2. (a) A TALENs construct (an engineered gene for nuclease enzymes) is inserted into a plasmid, which is then inserted into *Agrobacterium*, which delivers the plasmid to the soybean plants. The TALENs gene expresses the nucleases to silence the FAD2-1 and FAD2-1B genes.
   (b) Root cells are screened for expression of TALENs expression and FAD2 mutations (silenced genes). Cells expressing mutations are selected, grown up and allowed to self fertilise to produce seed. The seed was grown and the plants tested to determine if the mutations are heritable. Plants with both mutations are retained and screened to identify plants without the TALENs construct. These plants are used to cultivate a line of non-transgenic plants carrying the FAD2-1A and FAD2-1B mutations.

3. *Agrobacterium tumefaciens* is a bacterium capable of transferring genes to plants because it carries a tumour inducing 'infective' plasmid. Its tumour-inducing Ti plasmid is modified to delete the tumour forming gene and insert the gene of interest.

4. Soybeans have been engineered for insecticide resistance and broad spectrum herbicide resistance.

5. (a) Grain size/number: More, larger grains will increase total yield.
   (b) Maturation rate: Faster maturation rate will produce yielding plants more quickly. A second crop could be produced in a season.
   (c) Pest resistance: Reduces losses to pests and increases the resources the plant can direct to yield.

---

75. Engineering a Solution: Food for the Masses (page 106)

1. The bacterium because it uses only one enzyme to facilitate multiple reactions. It is therefore simpler to use in the production of the modified plant.

2. The gene can be isolated by first identifying the associated enzyme and its amino acid sequence. From this, the mRNA sequence can be identified. The correct mRNA molecules can then be extracted and reverse transcriptase used to copy the mRNA into DNA. This can then be amplified.

   Or - Once the DNA sequence is identified, PCR primers can be produced that will anneal to the start sequences of the gene. The PCR product will be the targeted gene.

   Or - The gene can be identified from its protein product (as above). This can then be cut from the chromosome using restriction enzymes and amplified.

3. *Agrobacterium*. This bacterium can transfer DNA into plants, so that the cells will contain recombinant DNA.

4. A plasmid (the *Ti plasmid*) is removed from the *Agrobacterium*. Using restriction enzymes the plasmid is cut and the target DNA inserted (the tumor forming gene is removed). DNA ligase is used to attach the target DNA to the plasmid. The plasmid is then replaced into the *Agrobacterium*.

5. (a) *Agrobacterium* transfers the recombinant plasmid to the cells of the target plant.
   (b) The best stage of development for transformation is while the plant is in embryonic form. In this way a larger proportion of the plant cells will be affected and take up the new DNA. This will cause a much better result in the adult plant.

6. Transformed plants can be identified if an extra gene is inserted along with the target gene. This is normally a gene for drug resistance. Plants grown on agar impregnated with the chemical will grow only if they have taken up the new DNA. Those without won't grow.

7. A large number of plants can be produced using plant tissue culture or vegetative propagation. In this way many plants can be produced, which will lead to rapid dissemination of the transgenic stock.

76. The Ethics of GMO Technology (page 108)

1. (a) Advantage: Crop growers would not need to spray for crops pest as often.
   (b) Problem: Plants producing toxins as a pest resistance may cause health problems if eaten over a long period of time. Pest resistant plants could become a problem outside the crop field (as weeds).

2. (a) Plants and animals could be used to produce commercial quantities of pharmaceuticals at an affordable cost for medicinal or industrial use.
   (b) Concerns over animal welfare and the long term effects of genetic modification on the animals and plants.

3. In any order:
   (a) Enhancing wool production in sheep (yield and/or wool quality).
   (b) Use of livestock animals as biofactories by producing useful proteins in their milk (especially cattle, but also sheep and goats).

4. The widespread use of antibiotic marker genes in food crops for human consumption or stock food may give rise to antibiotic resistant strains of pathogenic bacteria. Restrained use of antibiotics is now considered essential in preventing large scale development of antibiotic resistance.

5. (a) Introduces nitrogen fixing ability in non-legumes thereby reducing the need for nitrogen fertilisers.
   (b) The bacterium would prevent attack on the seeds by pathogenic bacteria and fungi.

6. **Note**: This question was not intended to imply that ethical or moral concerns are any less real or valid than biological ones. It was merely an exercise in identifying the nature of the biological concerns.
   (a) Some points for discussion are:
   – The GM product or the GMO could have an undesirable effect on humans or other organisms.
   – That the genetic modification would spread uncontrollably into other organisms (breeding populations of the same or different species).
   – Consumer choice is denied unless adequate labelling protocols are in place. If everything contains GM products, there is no consumer choice.
   – General fear of what is not understood (fear of real or imagined consequences).
   – Objections on the grounds that it is ethically and morally wrong to tamper with the genetic make-up of an organism.
   – Generation of monopolies where large companies control the rights to seed supplies & breeding stock.
   (b) Those that pose a real biological threat are:
   – For plant GMOs, the indiscriminate spread of transgenes.
   – Physiological reactions e.g. allergies, to novel proteins.
   – Some animal rights issues may be justified if genetic modification causes impaired health.

77. Chapter Review (page 110)
No model answer. Summary is the student's own.

78. KEY TERMS AND IDEAS: Did You Get It? (page 112)

1. DNA amplification (B), DNA methylation (L), epigenetic modifications (K), gene expression (O), genome (F), multipotent (M), PCR (I), plasmid (J), pluripotent (N), recombinant DNA (D), restriction enzyme (E), stem cell (H), totipotent (C), transgenesis (G), vector (A).

2. (a) C is the father.
   (b) These two individuals are homozygous for one allele therefore for that allele one band shows instead of two.

3. (a) Unipotent: Any cell type that differentiates along a single lineage, e.g. cardiomyocytes (cardiac muscle cells)
   (b) Multipotent: Hematopoeitic stem cells from bone marrow, epithelial stem cells, bone stem cells, umbilical cord blood.
   (c) Pluripotent: Embryonic stem cells (ESC).
   (d) Totipotent: The zygte and its first few divisions. Meristematic tissue (root and shoot tips) in plants.

4. (a) The DNA must be unpacked (as euchromatin)
   (b) ii Histone acetylation

79. Sources of Genetic Variation (page 114)

1. (a) Genetic variation arises through mutation and sexual reproduction. Mutation is the source of all new alleles but sexual reproduction reshuffles alleles in different combinations in the offspring. Epigenetic factors (DNA modifications such as methylation not involving sequence changes) also contribute to differences in phenotype. In sexual reproduction, three processes contribute to variation: independent assortment of alleles in meiosis, exchange of alleles between non-sister chromatids in crossing over, and random fertilisation, which unites genetically different gametes.
   (b) The environment can contribute to the phenotype by altering the expression of the genotype. Often, it operates by facilitating or preventing achievement of genetic potential, e.g. stunted growth at altitude, or by altering gene expression during development, e.g. sex determination in reptiles.

2. (a) Variation is the raw material on which natural selection acts. Selection acts on the phenotype (being the result of genotype and environment). Selection acts for or against particular allele combinations, enhancing or reducing the representation of these in the next generation. Selection therefore sorts the variability in a gene pool and establishes adaptive phenotypes.
   (b) In a changing environment, some phenotypes (and their genotypes) will be more suited to the environment at the time than others. These phenotypes will become more abundant. However, an environmental change may favour other phenotypes so these may become more common. The variation provides opportunity for the environment to 'select' the best suited phenotype at the time.

3. Favourable mutations can spread through bacterial lineages by exchange of genes through conjugation. Once a lineage has acquired a mutation, it is passed by asexual reproduction.

4. **Continuous variation** is characterised by a large number of phenotypic variations (so that a large sample of the population would exhibit a normal distribution for the trait in question). **Discontinuous variation** is characterised by a limited number of phenotypic variants. **Note**: Traits exhibiting continuous variation are determined by a large number of genes and are also frequently influenced by environment. Traits exhibiting discontinuous variation are determined by a single gene (for which there may be several alleles)).

5. (a) Wool production: Continuous
   (b) Hand Span: Continuous
   (c) Blood groups: Discontinuous
   (d) Albinism: Discontinuous
   (e) Body weight: Continuous
   (f) Flower colour: Discontinuous

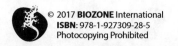
© 2017 **BIOZONE** International
ISBN: 978-1-927309-28-5
Photocopying Prohibited

80. Alleles (page 117)

1. (a) Heterozygous: Each of the homologous chromosomes contains a different allele for the gene (one dominant and one recessive).
   (b) Homozygous dominant: Each of the homologous chromosomes contains an identical dominant allele.
   (c) Homozygous recessive: Each of the homologous chromosomes contains an identical recessive allele.

2. (a) Aa   (b) AA   (c) aa

3. Each chromosome of a homologous pair comes from a different parent: one of maternal origin, one of paternal origin (they originated from the egg and the sperm that formed the zygote). They contain the same sequence of genes for the same traits, but the versions of the genes (alleles) on each chromosome may differ.

4. Alleles are different versions of the same gene. Different alleles provide phenotypic variation for the expression of a gene. There are often two alleles for a gene, one dominant and one recessive. In this case, the dominant allele will be expressed in the phenotype. Sometimes alleles for a gene can be equally dominant, in which case, both alleles will be expressed in the phenotype. Where three or more alleles for a gene exist in a population, there is more phenotypic variation in the population (for that phenotypic character) than would be the case if there were just two alleles.

81. Meiosis and Variation (page 118)

1. Crossing over reshuffles alleles between non-sister chromatids of homologous chromosomes and therefore unlinks linked genes. This increases the possible allele combinations in the gametes.

2. Independent assortment distributes of maternal and paternal homologues to the gametes independently of each other and so results in 2^n possible combinations of maternal and paternal chromosomes in gametes, where n is the haploid number, i.e. a very large number of possible combinations.

82. The Monohybrid Cross (page 119)

1. All the F_1 generation are heterozygous and thus display the dominant flower colour. When these are crossed together a 3:1 phenotypic ratio appears so that the homozygous recessive feature will be seen again.

2.

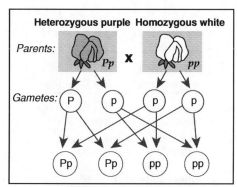

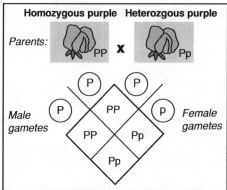

83. The Test Cross (page 302)

1. To perform the test cross here you would have to cross the male with a female (brown eye, ebony body) homozygous recessive for both genes (bbee).

   Note: Depending on the male's genotype the outcomes of the test cross would produce offspring that were:

   - All wild type (brown body, red eye)
   - Half wild type and half red eye, ebony body
   - Half wild type and half brown eye, brown body
   - 25% wild type, 25% red eye ebony, 25% brown eye, brown body, and 25% brown eye, ebony.

   Students could present this in Punnett squares.

Male gametes

	BE
eb	BbEe

red eye,
brown body

	BE	Be
eb	BbEe	Bbee

red eye,   red eye,
brown body   ebony body

	BE	bE
eb	BbEe	bbEe

red eye,   brown eye,
brown body   brown body

	BE	Be	bE	be
eb	BbEe	Bbee	bbEe	bbee

red eye,   red eye,   brown eye,   brown eye,
brown   ebony   brown   ebony
body   body   body   body

(Female gametes labelled on left side of squares)

2. A wild type male (brown or normal body and red eyes) could have one of four genotypes:
   BEBE, BEbE, BEBe, or BEbe

3. (a) 50% are wild type and 50% are red eye, ebony so the male must BEBe.
   (b) This is the only genotype that produces this ratio of phenotypes in the offspring (as per the second Punnett square above)

84. Practising Monohybrid Crosses (page 121)

2. (a) 50% BB 50% Bb
   (b) 100% black

3. (a) 25% BB 50% Bb 25% bb
   (b) 75% black 25% white

4. (a) 50% Bb 50% bb
   (b) 50% black 50% white

5. (a) 50%
   (b) 50%

6. (a) Bb
   (b) The black guinea pig must be Bb in order for there to be any white offspring. In this case, chance resulted in all the offspring born being white.
   (c) A test cross
   (d) Crossing to a homozygous recessive (white guinea pig) will reveal the genotype of the unknown parent. No white offspring would have been produced if the black guinea pig was BB.

85. Problems Involving Monohybrid Inheritance (page 122)

1. 1/2 Ww and 1/2 ww.

   Ratio: 1 wire-haired : 1 smooth haired

   Working: Parental genotypes are Ww X Ww. The test cross of the F₁ (to the homozygous recessive by definition) is to a smooth haired dog (ww).

   1/4 of the F₁ will be wire-haired (WW). When crossed with ww the result will be all wire-haired dogs (Ww).

   1/2 the F₁ will be wire-haired (Ww). When crossed with ww, the result is 1/2 wire-haired and 1/2 smooth-haired.

   1/4 of the F₁ will be smooth-haired (ww). When crossed with ww, all offspring will be smooth-haired (ww). Across all progeny, half will be Ww and half will be ww.

2. Probability of black offspring: (2/3 x 1/4=) 1/6 or 0.16

   Working: The parents genotypes are Bb X Bb, and 1/3 of the white offspring (BB) crossed with Bb will result in no black lambs while 2/3 of the white offspring (Bb) crossed with Bb will result in 1/4 black lambs.

3. (a) They have an albino child (aa) as well as unaffected ones (AA or Aa), so the parents must both be Aa. **Note:** There is a 25% chance that any child of theirs will be albino.
   (b) The family are all aa.
   (c) The albino father must be aa. The mother must be Aa. The three unaffected children are Aa.
   Note: There is a 50% chance that any child of theirs will be albino. The observed 3:1 ratio is not surprising, given the small number of offspring.

4. – **Couple #1** genotypes must be XᴴX– and XᴴY because neither is affected. Their son is affected XhY. If the mother is XᴴXᴴ they could not have an affected son. If she is XᴴXʰ, there is a 50% chance that her son will be XhY.
   – **Couple #2** genotypes must be XᴴX– and XʰY and their son is XᴴY. The father did not pass an X chromosome to his son, so his genotype is irrelevant. If the mother is XᴴXᴴ, all of her sons will be XᴴY, but if she is a carrier XᴴXʰ, there is a 50% chance that her son will be XʰY.
   – Either the hospital or the parents could be correct. The answer depends on the genotype of the mothers.

5. There is a possibility that the male is the father of the child as blood group O can result from crossing AO and BO genotypes. However there are also many other possible outcomes. Without more precise testing or knowing the actual genotypes of the male and female it is impossible to conclusively say the male is the father of the child.

86. Codominance of Alleles (page 123)

1. Two or more alleles are dominant over any recessive alleles and both are fully expressed.

2. (a) Diagram labels:

	White bull	Roan cow
Parent genotype:	CᵂCᵂ	CᴿCᵂ
Gametes:	Cᵂ, Cᵂ	Cᴿ, Cᵂ
Calf genotypes:	CᴿCᵂ, CᵂCᵂ	CᴿCᵂ, CᵂCᵂ
Phenotypes:	roan, white	roan, white

   (b) Phenotype ratio: 50% roan, 50% white (1:1)
   (c) By breeding only from the roan calves. Offspring of roan parents should include white, roan, and red phenotypes. By selecting only the red offspring from this generation it would be possible to breed a pure herd of red cattle.

3. (a) Diagram labels:

	Unknown bull	Roan cow
Parent genotype:	CᴿCᴿ	CᴿCᵂ
Gametes:	Cᴿ, Cᴿ	Cᴿ, Cᵂ
Calf genotypes:	CᴿCᴿ, CᴿCᵂ	CᴿCᴿ, CᴿCᵂ
Phenotypes:	red, roan	red, roan

   (b) Unknown bull: red bull

4. The phenotypic ratio would be 1 red: 2 roan: 1 white

87. Codominance in Multiple Allele Systems (page 124)

1. Blood group table:
   Blood group **B** BB, BO
   Blood group **AB** AB

2. | Cross 2 | Group O | Group O |
   |---|---|---|
   | Gametes: | O, O | O, O |

   Children's genotypes: OO, OO, OO, OO
   Blood groups: O, O, O, O

Cross 3	Group AB	Group A
Gametes:	A, B	A, O

   Children's genotypes: AA, AO, BA, BO
   Blood groups: A, A, AB, B

Cross 4	Group A	Group B
Gametes:	A, A	B, O

   Children's genotypes: AB, AO, AB, AO
   Blood groups: AB, A, AB, A
   Note: Answers can be arranged differently depending on which gamete circle each allele symbol is placed. There are many more crossover combinations possible.

3. (a) | Parent genotype: | AO | OO |
   |---|---|---|
   | Gametes: | A, O | O, O |
   | Children's genotypes: | AO, AO | OO, OO |
   | Blood groups: | A, A | O, O |

   (b) 50%
   (c) 50%
   (d) 0%

4. (a) Possible parent genotypes: Mother assumed to be heterozygous to get maximum variation in gametes (homozygous would also work).

Phenotypes	Group A	Group O
Genotypes:	AO	OO
Gametes:	A, O	O, O

   Child's genotype would have to be AO or OO.
   (b) The only possible offspring from this couple would have been children with group A or group O. The man making the claim could not have been the father of the child.

5. (a) Male
   (b) Child 1 (blood type B) could be BB or BO, whereas child 2 (blood type AB) can only have alleles A and B.

88. Dihybrid Cross (page 126)

Cross No. 1:

1. | | BL | Bl | bL | bl |
   |---|---|---|---|---|
   | **bL** | BbLL | BbLl | bbLL | bbLl |
   | **bL** | BbLL | BbLl | bbLL | bbLl |
   | **bl** | BbLl | Bbll | bbLl | bbll |
   | **bl** | BbLl | Bbll | bbLl | bbll |

2. Genotypes: BbLL 2 BbLl 4   bbLl 4 bbLL 2
   Bbll 2   bbll 2

3. Phenotypes: 6 black/short 6 white/short
   2 black/long   2 white/long

Cross No. 2:

4. Gametes: White parent: all bL
   Black parent: Bl, Bl, bl, bl

5. | | bL |
   |---|---|
   | **Bl** | BbLl |
   | **bl** | bbLl |

6. Genotypes: BbLl 8   bbLl 8

7. Phenotypes: 8 black/short 8 white/short

89. Inheritance of Linked Genes (page 128)

1. Linkage refers to the situation where genes are located on the same chromosome. As a result, the genes tend to be inherited together as a unit.

2. Gene linkage reduces the amount of variation because the linked genes are inherited together and fewer genetic

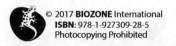

combinations of their alleles are possible.

3.

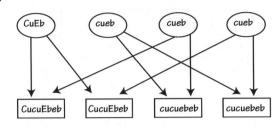

4. (a) CucuEbeb, Cucuebeb, cucuEbeb, cucuebeb
   (b) Offspring genotype: All CucuEbeb (heterozygotes)
       Offpspring phenotype: All wild type (straight wing, grey body)

5. Female gametes = VgEb and vgEb, Male gametes = vgeb
   Offspring genotypes: VgvgEbeb   vgvgEbeb
   Offspring phenotypes:
   Straight wing, grey body. Vestigial wing, grey body

6. *Drosophila* produce a wide range of mutations, have a short reproductive cycle, produce large numbers of offspring and are easy to maintain in culture.

90. Recombination and Dihybrid Inheritance (page 130)
1. It produces new associations of alleles in offspring.

2.

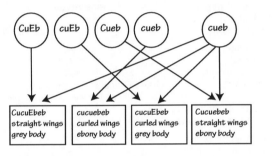

3. Parental linkage groups separate and new associations of alleles are formed in the offspring. The offspring show new combinations of characters that are unlike the parental types.

4. A greater than 50% recombination frequency indicates that there is independent assortment (the genes must be on separate chromosomes).

5. Female gametes: CuY , cuY
   Male gametes: Cuy, cuy
   Offspring genotypes and phenotypes:
   CuCuYy, CucuYy, CucuYy: Straight wings grey body
   cucuYy: Curly wings grey body

91. Detecting Linkage in Dihybrid Crosses (page 132)
1. Expected ratios as follows:
   Purple, long (P_L_)   215
   Purple, round (P_ll)   71
   Red, long (ppL_)   71
   Red, round (ppll)   24
   Total 381

2. (a) Expected ratios all 710 for each genotype as a 1:1:1:1 ratio is expected.
   (b) Parental (given), recombinant, recombinant, parental.
   (c) Morgan performed a test cross.

3. (a) Nail-patella syndrome is dominant. We can tell this because nearly all of the affected individuals had at least one parent with the disease.
   (b) The affected parent was blood group B. All of their offspring with the B blood group also had nail-patella syndrome. Therefore, nail-patella syndrome is linked to the B blood group allele.
   (c) Individual III-3 does not have nail-patella syndrome despite having the B blood type. It is likely that

recombination has occurred, so this individual has not received the nail-patella gene.

93. Using Chi-Squared in Genetics (page 134)
1. (a) H_0: "If both parents are heterozygous and there is independent assortment of alleles then we would expect to see a 9:3:3:1 ratio of phenotypes in the offspring".
   (b) H_A: "If both parents are heterozygous and the genes are linked (i.e. on the same chromosome), then we would expect the ratios of phenotypes in the offspring to deviate from the 9:3:3:1".

2. (a) Completed table:

Category	O	E	O – E	$(O-E)^2$	$\dfrac{(O-E)^2}{E}$
Purple stem, jagged leaf	12	16.3	–4.3	18.5	1.1
Purple stem, smooth leaf	9	5.4	3.6	13	2.4
Green stem, jagged leaf	8	5.4	2.6	6.8	1.3
Green stem, smooth leaf	0	1.8	–1.8	3.2	1.8
	Σ 29				Σ 6.6

   Expected frequencies calculated as follows:
   Purple stem, jagged leaf = 9/16 x 29 = 16.3
   Purple stem, smooth leaf = 3/16 x 29 = 5.4
   Green stem, jagged leaf = 3/16 x 29 = 5.4
   Green stem, smooth leaf = 1/16 x 29 = 1.8
   Note: Whole numbers could be used in preference to rounding to one decimal place.
   (b) χ^2 = 6.6
   (c) Degrees of freedom = (4-1=) 3
   (d) The critical value of χ^2 at P = 0.05 and at d.f.= 3 is 7.82. The calculated χ^2 value is less than the critical value (6.6 < 7.82).
   (e) We cannot reject H_0: There was no significant difference between the observed results and the expected phenotype ratio of 9:3:3:1. We must conclude that the genes controlling stem colour and leaf shape in tomatoes are on separate chromosomes (unlinked).

3. (a) H_0 and H_A as for question 1.
   (b) Completed table:

Category	O	E	O – E	$(O-E)^2$	$\dfrac{(O-E)^2}{E}$
Round-yellow seed	441	450	–9	81	0.18
Round-green seed	159	150	9	81	0.54
Wrinkled-yellow seed	143	150	–7	49	0.33
Wrinkled-green seed	57	50	7	49	0.98
	Σ 800				Σ 2.03

   Expected frequencies calculated as follows:
   Round-yellow seed = 9/16 x 800 = 450
   Round-green seed = 3/16 x 800 = 150
   Wrinkled-yellow seed = 3/16 x 800 = 150
   Wrinkled-green seed = 1/16 x 800 = 50
   χ^2 = 2.03

   (c) Degrees of freedom = (4-1) 3.
   The critical value of χ^2 at P = 0.05 and at d.f.= 3 is 7.82. The calculated χ^2 is less than the critical value (2.03 < 7.82).
   (d) We cannot reject H_0: There was no significant difference between the observed results and the expected phenotype ratio of 9:3:3:1. We must conclude that the genes controlling seed shape and colour are unlinked.

4. In both cases, we cannot reject H₀, but in the first case, the χ^2 value is much higher. In tomatoes, the genes for stem colour and leaf shape are on separate chromosomes, but given the relatively large χ^2 value, repeating the experiment with more plants, or replicates, would serve as a check.

94. Problems Involving Dihybrid Inheritance (page 135)

1. (a)

	BL	Bl
Bl	BBLl	BBll
bl	BbLl	Bbll

Genotype ratio: 1BBLl: 1BBll: 1BbLl: 1Bbll
Phenotype ratio: 1 black short hair, 1: black long hair

(b)

	TL	Tl	tbL	tbl
tbL	TtbLL	TtbLl	tbtbLL	tbtbLl
tbl	TtbLl	Ttbll	tbtbLl	tbtbll

Genotype ratio:
1TtbLL : 2TtbLl : 1Ttbll : 1tbtbLL : 2tbtbLl : 1tbtbll
Phenotype ratio: 3: Tabby long hair, 1:Tabby short hair,
3: blotched tabby long hair, 1: blotched tabby short hair

2. (a) Self pollination of plants with orange striped flowers produces progeny in ratios close to 9:3:3:1 (the expected ratio of a cross between heterozygous offspring of true breeding parents). Thus you may hypothesise that O (orange petals) is dominant to o (yellow petals) and stripes (S) are dominant to no stripes (s).
    (b) The plants with the orange striped flowers were genotype OoSs. You know this because OoSs x OoSs will produce the progeny phenotypes in the observed 9:3:3:1 ratio.

3. (a) bbSS (brown/spotted) X BBss (solid/black)
        (which parent was male and which female is unknown. Parents must be homozygous since all the offspring are of one type: BbSs: black spotted).
    (b) F₂ generation: BbSs X BbSs

	BS	Bs	bS	bs
BS	BBSS	BBSs	BbSS	BbSs
Bs	BBSs	BBss	BbSs	Bbss
bS	BbSS	BbSs	bbSS	bbSs
bs	BbSs	Bbss	bbSs	bbss

    (c) Spotted/black   9/16
         Spotted/brown   3/16
         Solid/black   3/16
         Solid/brown   1/16
         Ratio: 9:3:3:1 (described as above)

4. (a) F₁: Genotype: all heterozygotes RrBb.
    (b) F₁: Phenotype: all rough black coats.
    (c) F₂ generation: RrBb X RrBb

	RB	Rb	rB	rb
RB	RRBB	RRBb	RrBB	RrBb
Rb	RRBb	RRbb	RrBb	Rrbb
rB	RrBB	RrBb	rrBB	rrBb
rb	RrBb	Rrbb	rrBb	rrbb

    (d) Rough/black 9/16   Smooth/black 3/16
         Rough/white 3/16   Smooth/white 1/16
         Ratio: 9:3:3:1 (described as above)

    (e)

	RB	Rb	rB	rb
RB	RRBB	RRBb	RrBB	RrBb

    (f) F₂ Phenotype: all rough black coats.
    (g) The parents' genotypes: RrBb X Rrbb

        Explanation: Only these two genotypes crossed will produce all the phenotypes stated.

5. **Note**: Persian and Siamese parents are pedigrees (truebreeding) and homozygous for the genes involved.
    (a) Persian: UUss, Siamese: uuSS, Himalayan: uuss
    (b) F₁: Genotype: all heterozygotes UuSs.
    (c) F₁: Phenotype: all uniform colour, short haired.
    (d) F₂ generation: UuSs X UuSs

	US	Us	uS	us
US	UUSS	UUSs	UuSS	UuSs
Us	UUSs	UUss	UuSs	Uuss
uS	UuSS	UuSs	uuSS	uuSs
us	UuSs	Uuss	uuSs	uuss

    (e) 1:15 or 1/16 uuss: Himalayan
    (f) Yes (only one type of allele combination is possible)
    (g) 3:13 or 3/16 (2 uuSs, 1 uuSS)

6. (a) Yes
    (b) Four phenotypes were produced. If there was no crossing over there would only be two phenotypes (parental types).
    (c) CucuEbeb, cucuebeb, Cucuebeb, cucuEbeb.

---

95. Sex Linked Genes (page 137)

1. Parent genotype: XₒXₒ   XₒY
    Gametes: Xₒ, Xₒ   Xₒ, Y
    Kitten genotypes: XₒXₒ, XₒY, XₒXₒ, XₒY

Genotypes	Phenotypes
Male kittens: XₒY	Black
Female kittens: XₒXₒ	Tortoiseshell

2. Parent genotype: XₒXₒ   XₒY
    Gametes: Xₒ, Xₒ   Xₒ, Y
    Kitten genotypes: XₒXₒ, XₒXₒ   XₒY, XₒY
    Phenotypes: Orange female   Black male,
                            Tortoiseshell female   Orange male
    (a) Father's genotype: XₒY
    (b) Father's phenotype: Orange

3. Parent genotype: XₒXₒ   XₒY
    Gametes: Xₒ, Xₒ   Xₒ, Y
    Kitten genotypes: XₒXₒ, XₒY   XₒXₒ, XₒY
    Phenotypes: Tortoise female,   Tortoise female,
                            Black male   Black male
    (a) Father's genotype: XₒY
    (b) Father's phenotype: Orange
    (c) Yes, the same male cat could have fathered both litters.

4. Parent: Normal wife   Affected husband
    Parent genotype: XX   XᵣY
    Gametes: X, X   Xᵣ, Y
    Children's genotypes: XᵣX, XY   XᵣX, XY
    Phenotypes: Affected girl,   Affected girl,
                          Normal boy   Normal boy
    (a) Probability of having affected children = 50% or 0.5
    (b) Probability of having an affected girl = 50% or 0.5
         However, all girls born will be affected = 100%
    (c) Probability of having an affected boy = 0% or none

5. Parent: Affected wife   Normal husband
    Parent genotype: XᵣX   XY
    Gametes: Xᵣ, X   X, Y
    Children's genotype: XᵣX, XᵣY   XX, XY
    Phenotypes: Affected girl,   Normal girl,
                          Affected boy   Normal boy

    Note: Because the wife had a normal father, she must be heterozygous since her father was able to donate only an X-chromosome with the normal condition.
    (a) Probability of having affected children = 50% or 0.5
    (b) Probability of having an affected girl = 25% or 0.25
         However, half of all girls born may be affected.
    (c) Probability of having an affected boy = 25% or 0.25
         However, half of all boys born may be affected.

Background for question 6: Sex linkage refers to the location of genes on one of the sex chromosomes (usually the X, but a few are carried on the Y). Such genes produce an inheritance

© 2017 **BIOZONE** International
ISBN: 978-1-927309-28-5
Photocopying Prohibited

pattern that is different from that shown by autosomes:

- Reciprocal crosses produce different results (unlike autosomal genes that produce the same results).
- Males carry only one allele of each gene.
- Dominance operates in females only.
- A 'cross-cross' inheritance pattern is produced: father to daughter to grandson, etc.

6. **Sex linkage** (in humans, this usually means X-linkage) is involved in a number of genetic disorders. X-linked disorders are commonly seen only in males, because they have only one locus for the gene and must express the trait. If the sex linked trait is due to a recessive allele, females will express the phenotype only when homozygous recessive. It is possible for females to inherit a double dose of the recessive allele (e.g. a colour blind daughter can be born to a colour blind father and mother who is a carrier), but this is much less likely than in males because sex linked traits are relatively uncommon. Over a hundred X-linked genes are known, including those that control:

- Blood clotting: A recessive allele for this gene causes haemophilia. It affects about 0.01% of males but is almost unheard of in females.
- Normal colour vision: A recessive allele causes red-green colour blindness affecting 8% of males but 0.7% of females.
- Antidiuretic hormone production: A version of this gene causes some forms of diabetes insipidus.
- Muscle development: A rare recessive allele causes Duchene muscular dystrophy.

96. Inheritance Patterns (page 139)

1. Autosomal recessive:

(a) Punnett square:
Male parent phenotype:
Normal, carrier
Female parent phenotype:
Normal, carrier
(b) Phenotype ratio:
Normal 3   Albino 1

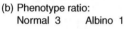

2. Autosomal dominant:

(a) Punnett square:
Male parent phenotype:
Woolly hair
Female parent phenotype:
Woolly hair
(b) Phenotype ratio:
Normal 1   Woolly 3

3. Sex linked recessive:

(a) Punnett square:
Male parent phenotype:
Normal
Female parent phenotype:
Normal, carrier
(b) Phenotype ratio:
Females:
Normal 2   Haemophiliac 0
Males:
Normal 1   Haemophiliac 1

4. Sex linked dominant:

(a) Punnett square:
Male parent phenotype:
Affected (with rickets)
Female parent phenotype:
Affected (with rickets)
(b) Phenotype ratio:
Females:
Normal 0   Rickets 2
Males:
Normal 1   Rickets 1

97. Pedigree Analysis (page 140)

Note: Strictly speaking, the allele for lactose tolerance is the faulty allele as this mutation occurred about 10,000 BC and causes the gene to fail to switch off. However, because it is so widespread, lactose intolerance is now often considered the 'faulty' state.

1. Autosomal recessive traits
(a) Genotypes of individuals on the chart:

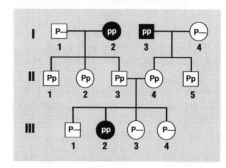

(b) The genotypes of parents II-3 and II-4 have to be carriers (heterozygous) because they produced an affected offspring (homozygous recessive). Alternatively, we know that they must be carriers because each had an affected parent (I-2 and I-3).

2. Sex-linked recessive traits
(a) Genotypes of individuals on the chart:

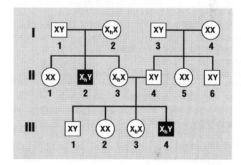

(b) Males have only one X chromosome. If that single chromosome carries the affected allele, then it will be expressed. Males cannot be heterozygous, since they can only carry one copy of the gene.

3. Autosomal dominant traits
(a) Genotypes of individuals on the chart:
Note: Parent I-2 has to be heterozygous (Ww) since some of the offspring are normal (ww). This could not occur if I-2 was homozygous dominant (WW).

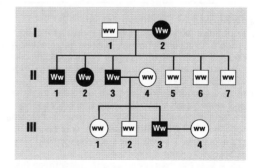

(b) Each affected individual has an affected parent.

4. Sex-linked dominant traits
    (a) Genotypes of individuals on the chart:

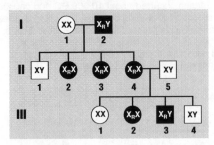

(b) Females have two X chromosomes, and so have a greater probability that one of them will carry the affected gene.

5. Suggestions for interpreting a pedigree chart. Students can come up with their own list of guidelines:

    If most of the males in the pedigree are affected, then the disorder is X-linked.
    If it is a 50/50 ratio between men and women the disorder is autosomal.
    If the disorder is dominant, one of the parents must have the disorder.
    If the disorder is recessive, neither parent has to have the disorder because they can be heterozygous (carriers).

    Autosomal recessive
    • Appears in both sexes with equal frequency.
    • Trait tends to skip generations.
    • Affected offspring are usually born to unaffected parents.
    • When both parents are heterozygous, approximately 1/4 of the progeny will be affected.

    Autosomal dominant
    • Appears in both sexes with equal frequency
    • Both sexes transmit the trait to their offspring
    • Does not skip generations
    • Affected offspring must have an affected parent unless they posses a new mutation

    X-linked dominant
    • Both males and females are affected; often more females than males are affected.
    • Affected sons must have an affected mother.
    • Affected daughters must have either an affected mother or an affected father.
    • Affected fathers will pass the trait on to all their daughters.

    X-linked recessive
    • More males than females are affected.
    • Affected sons are usually born to unaffected (carriers) mothers, thus the trait skips generations.

98. Gene Pools and Evolution (page 142)

1. (a) **Population size**: Large population acts as a 'buffer' for random, directional changes in allele frequencies. A small population can exhibit changes in allele frequencies because of random loss of alleles (failure of an individual to contribute young to the next generation).
    (b) **Mate selection**: Random mating occurs in many animals and most plants. With 'mate selection', there is no random meeting of gametes, and certain combinations come together at a higher frequency than would occur by chance alone. This will alter the frequency of alleles in subsequent generations.
    (c) **Gene flow between populations**: Immigration (incoming) and emigration (outgoing) has the effect of adding or taking away alleles from a population that can change allele frequencies. In some cases, two-way movements may cancel, with no net effect.
    (d) **Mutations**: A source of new alleles. Most mutations are harmful, confer poor fitness, and will be lost from the gene pool over a few generations. Some may be neutral, conferring no advantage over organisms with

different alleles. Occasionally, mutations may confer improved fitness and will increase in frequency with each generation, at the expense of other alleles.
(e) **Natural selection**: Selection pressures will affect some allele types more than others, causing allele frequencies to change with each generation.

2. (a) Increase genetic variation: Gene flow (migration), large population size, mutation.
    (b) Decrease genetic variation: Natural selection, non-random mating (mate selection), genetic drift.

99. Changes in a Gene Pool (page 144)

1. This exercise (a)-(c) demonstrates how the allele frequencies change as different events take place:

Phase 1: Initial gene pool

This is the gene pool before any of the events take place:

	A	a	AA	Aa	aa
No.	27	23	7	13	5
%	54	46	28	52	20

Phase 2: Natural selection

The population is now reduced by 2 to 23. The removal of two homozygous recessive individuals has altered the allele combination frequencies (rounding errors occur).

	A	a	AA	Aa	aa
No.	27	19	7	13	3
%	58.7	41.3	30.4	56.5	13.0

Phase 3: Immigration / emigration

The addition of dominant alleles and the loss of recessive alleles makes further changes to the allele frequencies.

	A	a	AA	Aa	aa
No.	29	17	8	13	2
%	63	37	34.8	56.5	8.7

100. Hardy-Weinberg Calculations (page 145)

1. **Working**: $q= 0.1$, $p= 0.9$, $q^2= 0.01$, $p^2= 0.81$, $2pq= 0.18$
    Proportion of black offspring = $2pq + p^2$ x 100% = 99%;
    Proportion of grey offspring = q^2 x 100% = 1%

2. **Working**: $q= 0.3$, $p= 0.7$, $q^2= 0.09$, $p^2= 0.49$, $2pq= 0.42$
    (a) Frequency of tall (dominant) gene (allele): 70%
    (b) 42% heterozygous; 42% of 400 = **168**

3. **Working**: $q= 0.6$, $p= 0.4$, $q^2= 0.36$, $p^2= 0.16$, $2pq= 0.48$
    (a) 40% dominant allele
    (b) 48% heterozygous; 48% of 1000 = **480**.

4. **Working**: $q= 0.2$, $p= 0.8$, $q^2= 0.04$, $p^2= 0.64$, $2pq= 0.32$
    (a) 32% heterozygous (carriers)
    (b) 80% dominant allele

5. **Working**: $q= 0.5$, $p= 0.5$, $q^2= 0.25$, $p^2= 0.25$, $2pq= 0.5$
    Proportion of population that becomes white = 25%

6. **Working**: $q= 0.8$, $p= 0.2$, $q^2= 0.64$, $p^2= 0.04$, $2pq =0.32$
    (a) 80%   (c) 36%   (e) 96%
    (b) 32%   (d) 4%

7. **Working**: $q= 0.1$, $p= 0.9$, $q^2= 0.01$, $p^2= 0.81$, $2pq= 0.18$
    Proportion of people expected to be albino (i.e. proportion that are homozygous recessive) = 1%

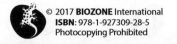
© 2017 **BIOZONE** International
ISBN: 978-1-927309-28-5
Photocopying Prohibited

101. Analysis of a Squirrel Gene Pool (page 147)

1. Graph of population changes:

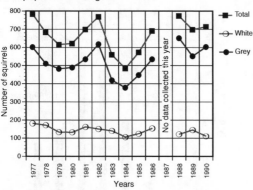

(a) 784 to 484 = 61% fluctuation
(b) Total population numbers exhibit an oscillation with a period of 5-6 years (2 cycles shown). Fluctuations occur in both grey and albino populations.

2. Graph of genotype changes:

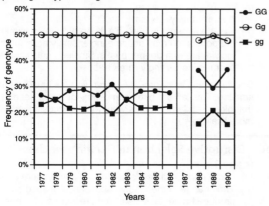

(a) GG genotype: Relatively constant frequency until the last 3-4 years, which show an increase. Possibly an increase over the total sampling period.
(b) Gg genotype: Uniform frequency.
(c) gg genotype: Relatively constant frequency until the last 3-4 years which exhibit a decline. Possibly a decrease over the total sampling period.

3. Graph of allele changes:

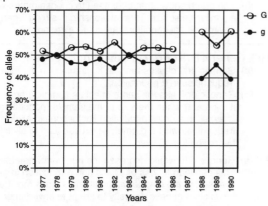

(a) Frequency of G: Increases in the last 3-4 years.
(b) Frequency of g: Decreases in the last 3-4 years.

4. (a) The *frequency of alleles* graph (to a lesser extent the *frequency of genotypes* graph)
(b) Changes in allele frequencies in a population bion provide the best indication of significant evolutionary changes occurring. These cannot be deduced simply from changes in numbers or genotypes.

5. There are at least two possible causes (any one of):
- Genetic drift in a relatively small population, i.e. there are random changes in allele frequencies as a result of small population size.
- Natural selection against albinos. Albinism represents a selective disadvantage in terms of survival and reproduction (albinos are more vulnerable to predators because of greater visibility and lower fitness).

103. Modelling Natural Selection (page 151)

There is no set answer to this activity. Students should notice that the phenotypes that stand out from the background become reduced in number over time.

104. Types of Natural Selection (page 152)

1. (a) Stabilising selection: Selection maintains the status quo. Phenotypes at the extremes of the current phenotypic mean are eliminated.
Stable environment and resources.
(b) Directional selection: Selection that eliminates phenotypes at one end of the phenotypic range and shifts the adaptive phenotype in one direction so that a new phenotypic norm is established.
Steady environmental trend (change in one direction, sometimes regionally).
(c) Disruptive selection: Selection that favours extremes of phenotype in the one environment and eliminates 'mid-range' phenotypes. Leads to two new phenotypic means.
Favoured in an environment where there is diversification of habitats or resources in the one place.

2. Fluctuating environments are more likely to provide resource instability (e.g. food shortages), which may favour diversification of phenotypes to exploit extremes of the resource range. For example, droughts may lead to seed shortages, so birds may be forced to exploit seeds outside the range of sizes they would normally eat (either small or large seeds), as occurred with the finches on Santa Cruz.

105. Stabilising Selection for Human Birth Weight (page 116)

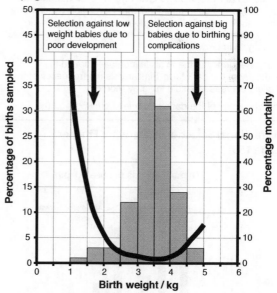

Note: Weight categories should not overlap. The data should be sorted into weight classes of: 0.0-0.49, 0.50-0.99 etc.

SAMPLE DATA: Use these data if students are unable to collect from local sources

3.740	3.830	3.530	3.095	3.630
1.560	3.910	4.180	3.570	2.660
3.150	3.400	3.380	2.660	3.375
3.840	3.630	3.810	2.640	3.955
2.980	3.350	3.780	3.260	4.510
3.800	4.170	4.400	3.770	3.400
3.825	3.130	3.400	3.260	4.100
3.220	3.135	3.090	3.830	3.970

© 2017 **BIOZONE** International
ISBN: 978-1-927309-28-5
Photocopying Prohibited

3.840	4.710	4.050	4.560	3.350
3.380	3.690	1.495	3.260	3.430
3.510	3.230	3.570	3.620	3.260
3.315	3.230	3.790	2.620	3.030
3.350	3.970	3.915	2.040	4.050
3.105	3.790	3.060	2.770	3.400
1.950	3.800	2.390	2.860	4.110
1.970	3.800	4.490	2.640	3.550
4.050	4.220	2.860	4.060	3.740
4.082	3.000	3.230	2.800	4.050
4.300	3.030	3.160	3.300	2.350
3.970	2.980	3.550	3.070	2.715

1. Normal distribution (bell-shaped curve), probably with a skew to the left.

2. 3.5 kg (taken from the table: only 2% mortality)

3. Good correlation. Lowest frequencies of surviving birth weights correspond to birth weights of highest mortality.

4. Selection pressures operate at extremes of the range: premature babies have reduced survival because their body systems are not fully developed; large babies present problems with delivery as the birth canal can only accommodate babies up to a certain (head) size.

5. Medical intervention can now allow babies that are very premature to survive (babies as small as 1.5 kg have a good chance of survival today, but this has not historically been the case). Caesarean deliveries have also allowed larger babies to be born. **Note**: This technology is available to wealthy societies thereby reducing the effect of this selection pressure. Developing countries still experience this selection pressure.

---

106. Directional Selection in Moths (page 154)

1. The appearance of the wings and body (how speckled and how dark the pigmentation).

2. The selection pressure (the differential effect of selective predation on survival) changed from favouring the survival of light coloured forms in the unpolluted environments (prior to the Industrial Revolution) to favouring the dark morph (over the light morph) during the Industrial Revolution (when there was a lot of soot pollution). In more recent times, with air quality improving, the survival of the light coloured forms has once again improved.

3. As the frequency of the M allele increased so did the frequency of the dark form. Similarly as the frequency of the m allele decreased so did the grey morph.

4. The frequency of the darker form fell from 95% to 50%.

---

107. Directional Selection in Darwin's Finches (page 155)

1. (a)

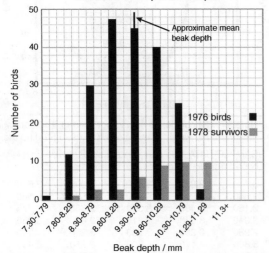

Number of birds per beak depth

2. (a) See graphs for means.
   (b) Approximately 0.5 mm
   (c) Yes, beak depth is heritable. If the drought continues the population may become increasingly dominated by individuals with deeper beaks. Smaller beak sizes will become increasingly rare or absent.

3. Smaller seeds were probably eaten first (as beaks were smaller). This left the birds competing for larger seeds such that birds with larger beaks were more successful and were more likely to survive.

---

108. Disruptive Selection in Darwin's Finches (page 156)

1. (a) Large and small seeds became relatively more abundant.
   (b) The change in the relative abundance of seed sizes produced a negative selection pressure on finches with intermediate sized beaks. Those with smaller and larger beaks fared better during the drought because they could exploit the smaller and larger seed sizes.

2. Beak size determines fitness, which shows a bimodal distribution. Birds with small beaks (-1.0 single measure) or larger beaks (single measure 1.25) show higher fitness (leave more offspring) than birds with intermediate beak sizes.

3. (a) Mate selection is non-random.
   (b) The graph shows that birds tend to choose mates with a similar beak size. This relationship is strong when the environmental conditions are more extreme.

---

109. Genetic Drift Affects Gene Pools (page 157)

1. (a) Genetic drift causes random fluctuations in the allele frequencies in a population.
   (b) Genetic drift has the same effect as sampling error, i.e. it is greater when the size of the sample (population) is small. In a small population fluctuations in allele frequencies will be greater, which can lead to alleles becoming lost or fixed.

2. (a) Genetic drift would decrease the number of heterozygotes.
   (b) This can lead to loss of alleles and a reduction in genetic diversity. In the long term, small populations may have insufficient genetic diversity to adapt to environmental changes.

---

110. The Founder Effect (page 158)

1.
Mainland	Nos	%		Nos	%
Allele A	48	54.5	Black	37	84
Allele a	40	45.5	Pale	7	16
Total	88	100			

Island	Nos	%		Nos	%
Allele A	12	75	Black	8	100
Allele a	4	25	Pale	0	0
Total	16	100			

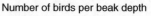

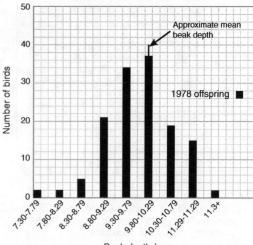

Number of birds per beak depth

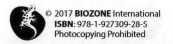

© 2017 **BIOZONE** International
ISBN: 978-1-927309-28-5
Photocopying Prohibited

2. The frequency of the dominant allele (A) is higher on the island population.

3. (a) Plants: Seeds are carried by wind, birds and water.
   (b) Animals: Reach islands largely by 'rafting' - situation where animals are carried offshore while clinging to vegetation; some animals survive better than others.
   (c) Non-marine birds: Blown off course and out to sea by a storm. Birds with strong stamina may survive.

4 Block A % for MDH-1 a in order 1-15: 61, 61, 64, 58, 61, 53, 68, 58, 56, 58, 56, 50, 50, 62, 25

   Block B % MDH-1 a in order 1-13: 19, 39, 25, 32, 30, 39, 30, 40, 42, 39, 46, 46, 53

5. Snails, although mobile, are restricted by their need for moisture. The tarmac roads and open areas on the blocks make movement between the two populations difficult as they are open and generally dry areas.

6. The frequencies have become different through a possible founder effect in which the original populations in each block had slightly different allele frequencies to begin with, or random events (i.e. genetic drift) have altered the proportion of alleles being passed to the next generation. Although adjacent, selection pressures in the blocks could also have been subtly different. It is likely that all these processes have contributed to the differences in allele frequencies.

7. Colony 15

111. Genetic Bottlenecks (page 160)

1. A population bottleneck is the sudden loss of a large part of the population (and their alleles) due to a large scale natural or human induced event.

2. When a population experiences a bottleneck, only a small proportion of the individuals survive, so their alleles are also lost. Even when the loss of individuals is non-selective, the population remaining is unlikely to retain all the alleles that were once present. If the loss was selective, e.g. individuals with a particular genetic makeup were able to survive an epidemic of disease, the individuals left will certainly not be genetically representative of the original population. Either way, genetic diversity in the bottlenecked population will be reduced relative to that of the original parent population.

3. Causes might be loss of the population via disease, hunting, or large sale environmental disaster (e.g. earthquake).

4. (a) There is very little genetic variation in the species, especially in the genes important in immune function.
   (b) The devils are so genetically similar that tissue from other Tasmanian devils is not recognised as foreign. This means cancerous tissue can spread between devils unchecked (without causing an immune reaction).

5. A sudden decrease in the size of a population can result in a corresponding reduction in genetic variation. This means the population has few 'genetic resources' to cope with the selection pressures imposed on it. This is evident in reduced reproductive success and a greater sensitivity to disease.

112. Chapter Review (page 162)
   No model answer. Summary is the student's own.

113. KEY TERMS AND IDEAS: Did You Get It? (page 164)
1. allele frequency (O), continuous variation (N), dihybrid cross (D), dominant (of alleles) (M), founder effect (F), genetic bottleneck (B), genetic drift (P), genotype E), independent assortment (G), monohybrid cross (J), mutation (K), natural selection (A), phenotype (H), recessive (of alleles) (C), recombination (I), sex linkage (L).

2. Directional selection describes the situation where a phenotype at one extreme of the phenotypic range has the greatest fitness, so the phenotypic norm shifts in the direction of that phenotype, e.g. selection for dark morphs of *Biston* moths in England during the Industrial Revolution. Stabilising selection describes the situation where fitness is highest for the most common phenotype and there is selection against

phenotypes at the extremes of the phenotypic range, e.g. selection for human birth weight.

3. (a) Recessive (bb) = 40%. bb = q^2 = 0.4.
   $q = \sqrt{0.4} = 0.63$.
   $p = 1 - q = 0.37$
   2pq (heterozygous) = 2 x 0.63 x 0.37 = 0.47 = 47%
   (b) $p^2 = 0.37^2 = 0.14$

4. (a) $M = \sqrt{0.49} = 0.7$
   (b) $N = \sqrt{0.09} = 0.3$ (or $q = 1- p = 1 - 0.7 = 0.3$)

114. Homeostasis (page 167)
1. Homeostasis is the relatively constant internal state of an organism, even when the external environment is changing. It is important for maintaining the suitable operating conditions for the body's metabolic systems, which are controlled by enzymes and require strict conditions of water potential, temperature, and pH.

2. (a) Detects a change in the environment and sends a message (electrical impulse) to the control centre.
   (b) Receives messages sent from the receptor, processes the sensory input and coordinates an appropriate response by sending a message to an effector.
   (c) Responds to the message from the control centre and brings about the appropriate response, e.g. muscle contraction or secretion from a gland.

115. Negative Feedback (page 168)
1. Negative feedback mechanisms are self-correcting (the response counteracts changes away from a set point) so that fluctuations are reduced. This stabilises physiological systems against excessive change and maintains a steady state.

2. A: Eating or food entering the stomach.
   B: Emptying of stomach contents.

116. Positive Feedback (page 169)
1. (a) Positive feedback has a role in amplifying a physiological process to bring about a particular response. Examples include (1) elevation in body temperature (fever) to accelerate protective immune responses, (2) positive feedback between oxytocin and uterine contractions: oxytocin causes uterine contraction and stretching of the cervix, which causes more release of oxytocin and so on until the delivery of the infant, (3) positive feedback in fruit ripening where ethylene accelerates the ripening of nearby fruit.
   Note: Not given as an example but there is also positive feedback between the hormone oestrogen and LH to leading to an LH surge and ovulation in mammals.
   (b) Positive feedback is inherently unstable because it causes an escalation in the physiological response, pushing it outside the tolerable physiological range. Compare this with negative feedback, which is self correcting and causes the system to return to the steady state.
   (c) Positive feedback loops are normally ended by a resolution of situation causing the initial stimulation. For example, in childbirth, once the infant is delivered, the stretching of the cervix ceases and so too does the stimulation for more oxytocin release.
   (d) When positive feedback continues unchecked, it can lead to physiological collapse. One example is unresolved fever. If an infection is not brought under control (e.g. by the body's immune system mechanisms or medical intervention), body temperature will continue to rise and can lead to seizures, neurological damage, and death.

© 2017 **BIOZONE** International
ISBN: 978-1-927309-28-5
Photocopying Prohibited

117. Hormonal Regulatory Systems (page 170)

1. (a) A hormone is a blood-borne chemical messenger secreted from an endocrine gland.
   (b) Hormones regulate the activities of cells and organs thereby maintaining homeostasis and bringing about important physiological events (such as reproduction).
   (c) Hormones are distributed in the bloodstream.
   (d) A hormone will only affect cells with the receptors specific to that particular hormone. Cells without the necessary receptors will be unaffected,

2. (a) Hormonal: Another hormone causes hormone release.
   (b) Humoral: A component in the blood (e.g. glucose) causes hormone release.
   (c) Neural: A nerve impulse stimulates hormone release.

118. What is Signal Transduction? (page 171)

1. (a) Reception: The signal molecule binds to the receptor on the cell surface.
   (b) Transduction: The activated receptor triggers a series of biochemical events within the cell (a signal cascade).
   (c) Response: The signal cascade results in a specific response in the target cell.

119. Modes of Hormone Action (page 172)

1. Intracellular receptors bind signal molecules that have passed through the plasma membrane. Extracellular receptors bind signal molecules outside the cell (on the cell's surface). The signal molecule does not cross the plasma membrane.

2. A signal molecule must bind to a receptor to activate it.

3. Hydrophobic signal molecules are able to freely cross the plasma membrane. Hydrophilic signal molecules are unable to cross the plasma membrane. They bind to extracellular receptors which transfer the signal to the cell's interior.

4. (a) A signal molecule binds to the extracellular receptor. A protein subunit is released from the intracellular part of the receptor. The protein activates a membrane-based enzyme. The enzyme produces a second messenger, which activates a signal cascade that ultimately ends with the activation of cell response.
   (b) A first messenger (e.g. peptide hormone) activates the extracellular receptor. A second messenger is intracellular and is activated after the extracellular receptor has responded to the first messenger. The second messenger conveys the signal to molecules inside the cell.

5. The signal molecule crosses the plasma membrane and activates the intracellular receptor. The receptor/signal complex then acts as a transcription factor, initiating transcription and bringing about the production of the protein product that is responsible for the cellular response.

6. (a) Extracellular signalling process. The signal molecule A is binding to an extracellular receptor.
   (b) An extracellular receptor
   (c) The signal molecule
   (d) A is a hydrophilic signal molecule. It cannot cross the plasma membrane and must activate the receptor to bring about signal transduction.

120. Auxins, Gibberellins, and Cytokinins (page174)

1. (a) Auxins: apical dominance and differential growth (as in phototropism), bud formation and fruit development. Antagonistic with cytokinins.
   (b) Gibberellins: Stem and leaf elongation by stimulating cell division and cell elongation. Breaking seed dormancy and promote growth of the embryo (germination).
   (c) Cytokinins: Promote axillary bud growth and cell division in shoots and roots. They moderate the effect of auxins (antagonistic) and delay leaf fall.

2. Auxins and cytokinins have antagonistic effects and certain ratios of auxin/cytokinin will stimulate lateral growth even when there is a growing shoot tip (showing apical dominance).

121. Plant Hormones as Signal Molecules (page 175)

1. Positive phototropism

2. In an experiment in which a cut stem with an auxin infused agar block is uppermost and an agar block without auxin is at the base, auxin moves down the stem. However, if the system is inverted, no auxin is found in the stem, indicating that the auxin in the agar was not transported or diffused through the stem - it only travels one way.

3. Auxin causes cell elongation.

122. The Role of Auxins in the Apical Dominance (page 176)

1. Auxins in the growing leaves of the apical bud are synthesised in concentrations high enough to suppress the growth of the buds below. Consequently, the main shoot grows more vigorously than the lateral shoots.

2. Auxin is produced in the growth regions of young plants (e.g. apical tip). If the apical tip of a young seedling remains intact, no lateral growth occurs. If the apical tip is removed, there is lateral growth. Conclusion: the presence of auxin in the apical tip of young seedlings inhibits lateral growth.

3. (a) and (b)

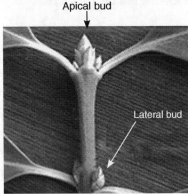

Apical bud

Lateral bud

   (c) The apical buds.
   (d) Their production of auxin inhibits the lateral buds so that the plant keeps growing upwards (towards light).

4. By nipping off the apical buds and encouraging lateral growth.

123. How Gibberellins Affect Growth (page 177)

1. and 2.

Table 1 Height of control / cm

	2	4	6	9	11	18	20
Mean	1.2	3.3	4.7	6.6	8.5	13.2	15.8
SD	0.5	0.3	0.4	0.4	0.8	2.0	2.6

Table 2 Height gibberellin treatment / cm

	2	4	6	9	11	18	20
Mean	0.8	5.8	14.0	23.4	26.6	33.5	35.2
SD	0.3	0.7	1.0	1.2	0.9	3.3	4.2

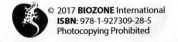

3 (a)

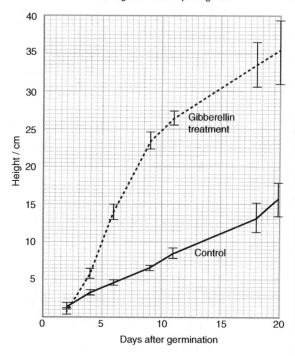

Effect of gibberellin on plant growth

(Graph: y-axis "Height / cm" from 0 to 40; x-axis "Days after germination" from 0 to 20. Two curves labelled "Gibberellin treatment" (dashed, upper) and "Control" (solid, lower), each with error bars.)

(b) Gibberellin increases the height of the plant.
(c) Yes
(d) The difference is significant as the error bars do not overlap between treatment and control.
(e) A Student's t - test could be used as there are two populations being investigated (control and gibberellin).
(f) $t = 8.78$. Degrees of freedom = 8. The difference is significant to $p = 0.001$

5. The peas do not produce gibberellins so when gibberellin is added the effect can be attributed to the treatment.

6. The peas with gibberellin will grow tall and the group with gibberellin and the inhibitor will show a result similar to the control because the gibberellin and gibberellin inhibitor will counteract each other to produce no additional growth effect.

124. The Effect of Gibberellin on Amylase Production
(page 179)
1. Seeds were soaked in distilled water to serve as a control (no gibberellin).

2. The halves containing the embryo were discarded because the embryo produces gibberellin and this source of the hormone must be removed (the only effects seen will be due to soaking in gibberellin).

3. The seeds soaked in water (control) showed no clearance zone on the starch agar. The seeds soaked in gibberellin had clearance zones around them where the starch had been hydrolysed. The gibberellin had stimulated the production of amylase enzyme in the seeds, which had diffused out to hydrolyse the starch in the starch agar.

Student's own responses:

4. Aim: to investigate the effect of gibberellin concentration on amylase production in germinating seeds.

5. Hypothesis: If the effect of gibberellin on amylase production in germinating seeds is related quantitatively, then higher concentrations of gibberellin will promote greater rate of amylase production and larger clearance zones on starch agar plates.

6. **Note**: Unit should be µmol dm^{-3} (first printing only).
(a) At least 4 concentrations in equal divisions (e.g. 0.25, 0.5, 0.75, 1.0 µmol dm^{-3}).
(b) Seeds soaked in distilled water.

7. Rinse the seeds in hypochlorite solution.

8. The embryo should be removed and only the half of the seed without the embryo used.

9. At least four. Five is probably better.

10. You could measure the physical extent of the clearance zone produced on the starch agar. However, it would be better to produce a calibration curve of amylase concentration against clearance zone measurement. This will allow you to equate any clearance zone extent with an amylase concentration. It would mean doing a preliminary plating with amylase solution.

11. In student's own words. Student choice regarding sample size and dilution series etc. Main points:

• 25 maize seeds, 5 soaked for 24 h in distilled water, and 5 each soaked for 24 h in prepared dilutions of a 1 µmol dm^{-3} stock solution of gibberellin.

• After 24 h, rinse all seeds in hypochlorite solution to sterilise. Wearing gloves, cut the seeds in half and discard the halves containing the embryo.

• Label each starch agar plate with the treatment (control, 0.25, 0.5, 0.75, 1.0 µmol dm^{-3}). Place the half grains containing the endosperms cut side down on starch agar plates (5 per plate).

• Incubate in the dark at room temperature for 24 h.

• Record the extent of the clearance zone on each plate. Obtain a mean for all 5 seeds per plate and use the calibration curve to equate this to an amylase concentration.

125. Photoperiodism in Plants (page 181)
1. (a) Pr (660nm) and Pfr (730nm).
(b) Pfr is the active form. In long day plants it promotes flowering. In short day plants it inhibits flowering.

2. (a) Pr converts rapidly to Pfr in natural light. Pfr coverts more slowly to Pr in darkness. The relative concentrations of Pr and Pfr give the plant the ability to measure day length. Phytochrome also interacts with clock genes, which maintain the plant's biological clock.
(b) The ability to measure time gives all the plants of a particular species the ability to determine the appropriate time for flowering. All plants will behave the same way and thus flower at the same time.

3. (a) Day length (more importantly, night length).
(b) Any one of:
    − Flowering at the same time ensures that other flowers will be available to provide/receive pollen.
    − Synchronisation with periods of high insect activity may assist pollination.

4. (a) Short-day plants: Flower only when the day length is short (average: 10 hours).
(b) Long-day plants: Flower only when the day length exceeds a certain minimum value (average: 14 hours).

5. Short-day plants are really long night plants, requiring a night length of more than a minimum value. In the experiment outlined, a short-day plant failed to flower when a long night was interrupted by a short period of light. The plant interpreted this as a short night irrespective of the short day prior to it.

126. The Mammalian Nervous System (page 183)
1. The three main functions of the nervous system is to detect stimuli, interpret them, and coordinate a response.

2. (a) **CNS**: Brain and spinal cord (nervous tissue extending down back and protected by the spinal column).
(b) The brain has ultimate control of almost all body activities (except simple spinal reflexes). The spinal cord interprets simple reflexes and relays impulses to and from the brain.

3. (a) **PNS**: All nerves and sensory receptors outside the CNS. Divided into sensory and motor divisions. The motor division controls both voluntary (somatic) and involuntary (autonomic) responses.
(b) Receives sensory information, relays impulses to the CNS, brings about the motor response.

4. Separation of the motor division of the PNS into somatic and autonomic divisions allows essential functions to occur without conscious involvement. In this way, the conscious part of the brain is not overwhelmed by having to coordinate every motor response. This improves efficiency of motor function.

5. The sympathetic NS is active when the body is preparing for fight or flight. The parasympathetic NS is more active in conserving energy and replenishing energy reserves ('feed or breed' or 'rest and digest').

127. The Autonomic Nervous System (page 185)

1. The sympathetic and parasympathetic divisions have broadly opposite actions. The sympathetic division predominates in preparation for fight or flight, whereas the parasympathetic division predominates in physiological functions associated with rest, digestion, and reproduction.

2. Two opposing systems regulate autonomic activities because functions that support fight or flight must be countered by functions that allow rest and recovery. One system would not provide the range of physiological functions needed to respond to changing environmental challenges.

3. Sympathetic stimulation causes release of noradrenaline from the adrenal glands, where it acts as a hormone and circulates affect a wide range of tissues and organs for a longer period of time. **Note:** compare this to parasympathetic stimulation (via acetylcholine), which is broken down rapidly at the synapse.

128. The Human Brain (page 186)

1. **A:** Cerebrum. Function: Higher thought processes (conscious thought).
    B: Cerebellum. Function: Coordinates body movements, posture and balance.
    C: Brainstem. Function: Acts as a relay centre between the brain and the spinal cord. Also is involved autonomic functions such as breathing, heart rate, and swallowing.
    D: Diencephalon (thalamus and hypothalamus). Thalamus acts as relay centre for sensory messages. Hypothalamus controls the autonomic nervous system and links nervous and endocrine systems. It regulates sleep, appetite, thirst and body temperature.

2. The medulla oblongata controls breathing, heart rate, and various other autonomic reflexes. If damaged, death is likely as these functions will be impaired.

3. The primary somatic sensory area receives information from the skin, muscles, and viscera. It allows recognition of pain, temperature, and touch.

4. The primary motor area controls muscle movement. Each side controls the activity on the opposite side of the body.

5. (a) Breathing/heartbeat: brainstem (medulla)
    (b) Memory/emotion: cerebrum
    (c) Posture/balance: cerebellum
    (d) Autonomic functions: hypothalamus
    (e) Visual processing: occipital lobe
    (f) Body temperature: hypothalamus
    (g) Language: motor and sensory speech areas
    (h) Muscular movement: primary motor area

129. Neurones (page 188)

1. (a) A motor neurone has four main regions, thin processes called dendrites at one end of the cell, a soma containing the nucleus, a long process (axon) extending from the soma, and axon branches with terminal synaptic knobs.
    (b) A neurone is specialised to process and transmit information as electrical impulses from the point of stimulus to the point of reception. Its dendrites receive information, the axon transmits the impulse, and the axon branches transmit the impulse to a receiving cell.

2. (a) A reflex is an involuntary response to a stimulus.
    (b) Reflexes allow very rapid responses to stimuli without involving higher brain function (thinking). This aids survival by ensuring appropriate responses to potentially dangerous stimuli are made as quickly as possible. Reflexes are also important in providing sensory feedback

during activities such as walking.

3. (a) Myelination increases the speed of impulse conduction.
    (b) Myelination prevents ion leakage across the neurone membrane. The current is carried in the cytoplasm so that the action potential at one node is sufficient to trigger an action potential at the next. Myelin also reduces energy expenditure since fewer ions overall need to be pumped to restore resting potential after an action potential passes.
    (c) Faster conduction speeds enable more rapid responses to stimuli.
    (d) 0-200 um diameter

130. Transmission of Nerve Impulses (page 190)

1. An action potential is a self-regenerating depolarisation that allows excitable cells (such as muscle and nerve cells) to carry a signal over a (varying) distance.

2. (a) Neurones are able to transmit electrical impulses.
    (b) Supporting cells are not able to transmit impulses.

3. (a) Depolarisation: Na^+ channels open and Na^+ ions flood into the cell.
    (b) Repolarisation: Na^+ channels close, K^+ channels open and K^+ ions move out of the cell.

4. (1) When the neurone receives the threshold-level stimulus, the membrane briefly becomes more permeable to Na^+, which floods into the cell, resulting in a depolarisation.
    (2) After the Na^+ influx, the Na^+ gates close and K^+ gates open, causing a brief hyperpolarisation before the resting potential is restored.
    (3) The hyperpolarisation means that for a short time (1-2 ms) the neurone cannot respond, so the impulse only travels in one direction (away from the stimulus).

5. Resting potential is restored by closure of the Na^+ channels and opening of the K^+ channels. K^+ moves out to restore the negative charge to the cell interior. All voltage activated gates close and the resting state is restored.

6. (a) Action potential travels by saltatory conduction, with depolarisation and action potential generation at the nodes of Ranvier.
    (b) Action potential spreads by local current (slower conduction speed).

7. Because the refractory period makes the neurone unable to respond for a brief period after an action potential has passed, the impulse can pass in only one direction along the nerve (away from the cell body).

131. Synapses (page 192)

1. A synapse is a junction between the end of one axon and the dendrite or cell body of a receiving neurone. A synapse can also occur between the end of one axon and a muscle cell (this is called the neuromuscular junction or motor end plate).

2. Arrival of a nerve impulse at the end of the axon causes a calcium influx. This induces the vesicles to release their neurotransmitter into the cleft.

3. Delay is caused by the time it takes for the neurotransmitter to diffuse across the synaptic cleft.

4. (a) The neurotransmitter is inactivated by an enzyme (for acetylcholine this acetylcholinesterase) or by active re-uptake of neurotransmitter into the presynaptic neurone (noradrenaline's effect at the synapse is terminated mostly by re-uptake but also by breakdown by the enzyme monoamine oxidase).
    (b) The neurotransmitter must be deactivated soon after its release to prevent continued stimulation of the post-synaptic cell (synaptic fatigue).
    (c) The presynaptic neurone releases the neurotransmitter and the postsynaptic neurone has the receptors to bind and respond to that neurotransmitter. The information flow can therefore only be in one direction.

5. They both involve release of the neurotransmitter acetylcholine in response to arrival of an action potential.

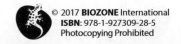

6. (a) Depolarisation
    (b) Hyperpolarisation
    (c) The response of the post-synaptic cell to the arrival of
        the neurotransmitter depends on the nature of the cell
        itself, on its location in the nervous system, and on the
        particular type of neurotransmitter involved.

7. Noradrenaline is a NT in the sympathetic division of the
    autonomic nervous system (sympathetic nervous system)
    and its effect at the synapse are excitatory. Acetylcholine is
    widespread with varying effects. It is the NT in all autonomic
    ganglia where it can be excitatory or inhibitory depending on
    the receptors present on the postsynaptic cells. It is the only
    NT in the somatic nervous system where its effects at the
    synapse are excitatory (e.g. in muscle contraction).

132. Integration at Synapses (page 194)

1. Integration enables the interpretation and coordination (by the
    central nervous system) of inputs from many sources (inputs
    may be inhibitory or excitatory).

2. (a) and (b) any two of:
    -   Chemical synapses transmit impulses in one direction to a
        precise location so information transfer is accurate.
    -   They rely on a limited supply of neurotransmitter so they
        are subject to fatigue (inability to respond to repeated
        stimulation). This prevents the system from over
        stimulation.
    -   Synapses also act as centres for the integration of inputs
        from many sources.

3. (a) Summation: The additive effect of presynaptic inputs
        (impulses) in the postsynaptic cell.
    (b) Spatial summation refers to the summation of impulses
        from separate axon terminals arriving simultaneously at
        the postsynaptic cell. Temporal summation refers to the
        arrival of several impulses from a single axon terminal in
        rapid succession (summing in time).

133. Drugs at Synapses (page 195)

1. An antagonistic drug decreases the usual effect of a
    neurotransmitter, whereas an agonistic drug increases the
    usual effect of a neurotransmitter.

2. Nicotine mimics the action of acetylcholine at autonomic
    ganglia and the motor end plate where it when it binds and
    causes excitation (depolarisation). Cobra venom also binds
    to acetylcholine receptors at the motor end plate but it blocks
    them so impulse generation is blocked. Hence it causes
    muscle paralysis.

3. Lidocaine binds to acetylcholine receptors on sensory
    neurones, stopping acetylcholine binding and blocking impulse
    transmission. Because signals from the sensory (pain)
    neurones are blocked, lidocaine acts as a local anaesthetic.

134. The Basis of Sensory Perception (page 196)

1. Sensory receptors convert stimulus energy (e.g.
    electromagnetic radiation) into electrochemical energy (a
    change in membrane potential).

2. All receptors receive and respond to stimuli by producing
    receptor potentials.

3. The stimulus energy opens an ion channel in the membrane
    leading to ion flux and a localised change in membrane
    potential, e.g. an influx of Na^+ and a depolarisation. This
    localised change in membrane potential is called a receptor
    potential and it may lead directly or indirectly to an action
    potential.

4. Receptor potentials are localised depolarisations. They are
    graded (of different sub-threshold magnitude) and not self-
    propagating.

135. The Structure of the Eye (page 197)

1. The two types of photoreceptor cells are rods, which are
    the most numerous and are located on the outer edges of
    the retina, and cones, which are less numerous and are

concentrated in the central fovea of the retina.

2. The incoming light is refracted (primarily by the cornea) and
    the amount entering the eye is regulated by constriction
    of the pupil. The degree of refraction is adjusted through
    accommodation (changes to the shape of the lens) so that a
    sharp image is formed on the retina.

3. (a) The photoreceptor cells contain photosensitive pigments
        which absorb the light and convert it to an electrical
        response. **Note**: Recall that sensory receptors are
        biological transducers and convert one type of stimulus
        energy to another.
    (b) We see images the right way up because the visual
        processing centre in the brain interprets the impulses it
        receives and corrects the orientation of the image.

136. The Physiology of Vision (page 198)

1. (a) The retina is the region of the eye responsible for
        receiving and responding to light. It contains the pigment-
        containing photoreceptor cells (the rods and cones) which
        absorb the light and produce an electrical response. This
        response is converted by other cells in the retina into
        action potentials in the optic nerve.
    (b) The optic nerve is formed from the axons of the retinal
        ganglion cells, and carries the action potentials from the
        retina through the optic chiasma to the visual cortex in the
        cerebrum.
    (c) The central fovea is the region of the retina with the
        highest cone density where acuity is greatest (sharpest
        vision).

2.
Feature	Rod cells	Cone cells
Visual pigment(s):	Rhodopsin (no colour vision)	Iodopsin (three types)
Visual acuity:	Low	High
Overall function:	Vision in dim light, high sensitivity	Colour vision, vision in bright light

3. (a)-(c) in any order
    (a) **Photoreceptor cells** (rods and cones) respond to light by
        producing graded receptor potentials.
    (b) **Bipolar neurons** form synapses with the rods and cones
        and transmit the changes in membrane potential to the
        ganglion cells. Each cone synapses with one bipolar
        (=high acuity) whereas many rods synapse with one
        bipolar cell (=high sensitivity).
    (c) **Ganglion cells** synapse with the bipolar cells and
        respond with depolarisation and generation of action
        potentials. Their axons form the optic nerve.

4. (a) **Horizontal cells** are interconnecting neurons that
        help to integrate and regulate the input from multiple
        photoreceptor cells. They give information about contrast.
    (b) **Amacrine cells** form synapses with bipolar cells and work
        laterally to affect output from the bipolar cells, enhancing
        information about light level.

5. Several rod cells synapse with each bipolar cell. This gives
    poor acuity but high sensitivity. Each cone cell synapses
    with only one bipolar cell and this gives high acuity but poor
    sensitivity.

6. (a) A photochemical pigment is a molecule (e.g. contained in
        the membranes of the photoreceptor cells) that undergoes
        a structural change when exposed to light (and is
        therefore light-sensitive).
    (b) Rhodopsin in rods and iodopsin in cones.

7. Light falling on the retina causes structural changes in
    the photopigments of the rods and cones. These changes
    lead to the development of graded electrical signals
    (hyperpolarisations) which spread from the rods and cones,
    via the bipolar neurons, to the ganglion cells. The ganglion
    cells respond by depolarisation and transmit action potentials
    to the brain.

© 2017 **BIOZONE** International
ISBN: 978-1-927309-28-5
Photocopying Prohibited

137. Extrinsic Control of Heartbeat (page 200)

1. (a) Increased venous return: Heart rate increases.
    (b) Release of adrenaline: Heart rate increases.
    (c) Increase in blood CO_2: Heart rate increases.

2. These effects are brought about by the cardiovascular centre (sympathetic output via the cardiac nerve).

3. Physical exercise increases venous return.

4. (a) Cardiac nerve   (b) Vagus nerve

5. (a) Baroreceptors respond to changes in blood pressure.
    (b) Chemoreceptors respond to changes in blood chemistry (H^+ or CO_2 concentration). **Note**: Those in the aorta respond to changes in CO_2, but not pH, while the carotid body detects changes in both.

138. The Liver's Role in Protein Metabolism (page 201)

1. Aspects of protein metabolism (a-c in any order):
    (a) Transamination of amino acids to create new, non-essential amino acids.
    (b) Deamination of excess amino acids and production of urea in the urea cycle.
    (c) Synthesis of plasma proteins.

2. Deamination produces keto acids and an amino group. The keto acids feed into the Krebs cycle and are oxidised to yield ATP. NH_2 is converted to ammonia (toxic) and joins with CO_2 and enters the orninthine cycle to produce urea.

3. (a) Ammonia is highly toxic.
    (b) It is converted to less toxic urea, which can be transported in the blood and excreted at the kidneys.

139. The Urinary System (page 202)

1. (a) Kidney: produces urine and regulates blood volume.
    (b) Ureters: convey urine to the bladder
    (c) Bladder: stores urine
    (d) Urethra: conveys urine to the outside of the body
    (e) Renal artery: carries blood from aorta to kidney. Supplies the kidney with blood carrying oxygen and urea.
    (f) Renal vein: carries blood from kidney to vena cava. Returns blood from the kidney to the venous circulation.
    (g) Renal capsule: covers the kidney and protects it against trauma and infection.

2. 99.4%

3. (a) A nephron is the selective filtering element in the kidney. It is the functional unit of the kidney.
    (b) The nephron produces a filtrate from the blood, modifies the filtrate and produces the final excretory fluid (urine).

4. Student's own drawing.

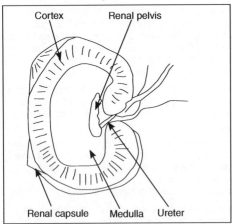

Cortex   Renal pelvis

Renal capsule   Medulla   Ureter

140. The Physiology of the Kidney (page 204)

1. The high blood pressure is needed for ultrafiltration, i.e. to force small molecules such as water, glucose, amino acids, sodium chloride and urea through the capillaries of the glomerulus and the basement membrane and epithelium of Bowman's capsule.

2. (a) Glomerular filtration: Produces an initial filtrate of the blood that is similar in composition to blood and can be modified to produce the final urine.
    (b) Active secretion: Secretion allows the body to get rid of unwanted substances into the urine.
        Explanatory detail: Active secretion of chloride in the ascending limb (with sodium following passively) contributes to the maintenance of the salt gradient in the extracellular fluid (this gradient allows water to be reabsorbed in the collecting duct). Secretion of toxins and unwanted ions into the filtrate in the distal tubules allows the blood composition to be adjusted and poisons to be excreted. Energy is used to secrete these substances against their concentration gradients
    (c) Reabsorption: Essential process that allows the useful substances (required by the body) to be retained from the filtrate (particularly the initial filtrate, where 90% is reabsorbed). The body would waste energy if these substances were not retained.
    (d) Osmosis: Osmotic loss of water allows the urine to be concentrated (via loss of water).
        Explanatory detail: Osmosis is important in two regions of the nephron: In the descending limb of the loop of Henle, osmotic loss of water concentrates the filtrate so that salt can be withdrawn from the ascending limb to contribute to the salt gradient in the extracellular fluid. In the collecting duct, loss of water by osmosis provides the final concentration of the urine

3. (a) The salt gradient allows water to be withdrawn from the urine (allows the urine to be concentrated). **Explanatory detail**: Because the salt gradient increases through the medulla, the osmotic gradient is maintained and water can be continually withdrawn from the urine (countercurrent system operates).
    (b) Salt gradient is produced by the active and passive movement of salt from the filtrate into the extracellular fluid in the medulla.

141. Control of Urine Output (page 206)

1. (a) ADH secretion increases: urine volume decreases, blood volume increases.
    (b) ADH secretion decreases: urine volume increases, blood volume decreases.

2. Diabetes insipidus symptoms include the excretion of large amounts of very dilute urine (accompanied by a great thirst).

3. Alcohol inhibits ADH release causing greater urine output, resulting in dehydration and thirst.

4. (a) Aldosterone increases the reabsorption of sodium from the kidney tubules.
    (b) Water follows sodium reabsorption, increasing blood volume.

5. Decreases or increases in blood volume are detected by hypothalamic osmoreceptors and the secretion of ADH increases or decreases accordingly. This results in an adjustment of urine output until homeostasis is restored. The adjustments made in response to the ADH release act back on the hypothalamus to counter further change. Note that, by a more complex mechanism, low blood volumes also stimulate the release of aldosterone, which induces Na^+ reabsorption in the kidney and (by osmosis) more absorption of water and thus restoration of blood volume.

© 2017 **BIOZONE** International
ISBN: 978-1-927309-28-5
Photocopying Prohibited

142. Adaptations for Conserving Water (page 207)

1. (a) Water requirement per day = 60 cm^3.

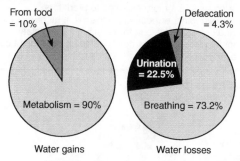

From food = 10%

Metabolism = 90%

Water gains

Defaecation = 4.3%

Urination = 22.5%

Breathing = 73.2%

Water losses

Water requirement per day = 60 cm^3

(b) Humans obtain water primarily by drinking. Kangaroo rats obtain water from metabolism and don't need to drink.
(c) Kangaroo rats can produce a very concentrated urine.

2. (a)-(c) any three of the following:
   - Able to meet most of their water requirements from oxidation of dry foods (metabolism).
   - Kidneys are able to produce very concentrated urine (long loop of Henle in the nephrons).
   - Reduce losses from breathing by reabsorbing moisture in the nasal passages.
   - Faeces egested as very dry pellets.
   - Do not need to sweat or pant to keep cool.

3. Kangaroo rats are nocturnal and reman underground during the day when water losses would be greatest.

4. Most mammals need to drink regularly to replace losses through urination, defecation, and sweating.

5. (a) The loop of Henle in the nephrons of kangaroo rats is nearly three times the length of that in humans.
   (b) The longer the loop of Henle, the more the urine can be concentrated. Because the osmotic withdrawal of water operates on a countercurrent system, the greater the gradient, the greater the distance over which a concentration gradient can be maintained for the osmotic withdrawal of water.
   (c) The salt gradient allows water to be withdrawn from the urine (allows the urine to be concentrated). Note: Apologies for this question duplication, which will be removed in subsequent revisions.

143. Endothermy vs Ectothermy (page 209)

1. Ectotherms depend on the environment for their heat. Endotherms generate heat from their internal metabolism.

2. (a) The lizard (ectotherm)
   (b) By basking in the sun (to heat up) and retreating to shade (to cool down).
   (c) Eating and exercise cause a rise in body temperature.
   (d) Sleeping generally causes the reduction of body temperature.

3. (a) Allowing body temperature to fall saves energy because the animal does not have to maintain body temperature against environmental variation.
   (b) Ectothermy saves energy because ectotherms are not physiologically committed to maintaining a high metabolic rate. Lower metabolic rates are advantageous when food supplies are low (less energy is required for maintenance).

4. (a) Raising body temperature quickly is important as it allows activity, e.g. for hunting or escaping danger. It also increases the rate and efficiency of metabolic processes such as digestion.
   (b) Panting causes evaporative cooling and helps to keep the temperature of the brain lower than the rest of the body.

5. (a) Optimum temperature range for an endotherm is from 18° or 19°C to 36°C. Between these temperatures, oxygen consumption, and therefore energy expenditure, is lowest.
   (b) Below 15°C more energy is required to maintain body temperature against heat loss. Above 35°C, more energy is used to dissipate excess heat.
   (c) Warming the body, e.g. by shivering, requires muscle movement. Panting requires muscle movement. Cooling by sweating uses cellular energy because secretion (of sweat) is an active process.

144. Thermoregulation in Humans (page 211)

1. (a) In the hypothalamus.
   (b) The hypothalamus acts as a thermostat, registering changes in body temperature and coordinating responses to maintain its set point.

2. (a) **The skin**: Receptors in the skin detect changes in skin temperature and relay the information to the hypothalamus. In response to hypothalamic output, muscles and capillaries in the skin bring about an appropriate response (e.g. shivering or sweating).
   (b) **The muscles**: Muscles begin rapid contractions (shivering) when the body temperature drops too far. The activity generates heat which warms the body.
   (c) **The thyroid gland**: When the body temperature becomes too low the thyroid gland releases hormones that increase the body's metabolic rate (generating heat).

3. Negative feedback acts to counteract deviations from the set point temperature of 36.7°C. Movement away from the set point in either direction triggers corrective mechanisms, which then return the body temperature to the set point.

4. (a) An infection causes the thermoregulatory set point in the hypothalamus to be reset to a higher temperature, resulting in a higher body temperature.
   (b) It is a defence against infection (helps to speed up the immune response and kills the infectious organism more quickly).
   (c) Fever raises the body above the normal set point temperature. Prolonged elevated body temperature can result in a positive feedback loop, which causes body temperature to escalate, denaturing enzymes and detrimentally affecting normal metabolic processes.

5. Wind chill, very low temperatures, being wet, inactivity, inadequate clothing (reduced insulation).

6. Excessive activity, excessive clothing (too much insulation), being excessively overweight, high temperature environment.

145. The Role of the Skin in Thermoregulation (page 213)

1. Blood vessels can constrict (reduce blood flow) or dilate (increase blood flow) to regulate the amount of blood flowing from the body to the skin and back. This regulates temperature by regulating the amount of heat moving from the body's core to the skin's surface where heat is lost.

2. People who have grown up in cold climates have a reduced ability to sweat. Sweating is uneven and beads, so it drips from the body rather than evaporating and removing excess heat energy. As a result they over-heat easily.

146. Chapter Review (page 214)

No model answer. Summary is the student's own.

© 2017 **BIOZONE** International
ISBN: 978-1-927309-28-5
Photocopying Prohibited

147. KEY TERMS AND IDEAS: Did You Get It? (page 216)
1. acetylcholine (C), autonomic nervous system (J), auxin (N), central nervous system (B), cerebrum (F), gibberellin (M), homeostasis (L), hormone (O), hypothalamus (K), parasympathetic nervous system (E), retina (I), second messenger (A), stimulus (D), sympathetic nervous system (G), thermoregulation (H).

2. (a)

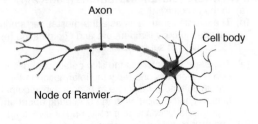

Axon
Cell body
Node of Ranvier

   (b) Myelinated
   (c) Schwann cells can be seen wrapped around the axon. Nodes of Ranvier can also be seen.

3. (a) Kidney
   (b) Nephron
   (c) Loop of Henle
   (d) Antidiuretic hormone

4. (a) Negative feedback
   (b) Outcome: Has a stabilising effect, Maintains a steady state by counteracting variations from the normal set point.

148. Components of an Ecosystem (page 219)
1. A community is a naturally occurring group of organisms living together as an ecological entity. The community is the biological part of the ecosystem. The ecosystem includes all of the organisms (the community) and their physical environment.

2. The biotic factors are the influences that result from the activities of living organisms in the community whereas the abiotic (physical) factors comprise the non-living part of the community, e.g. climate.

3. (a) Population   (c) The community
   (b) Ecosystem   (d) Physical factor

149. Types of Ecosystems (page 220)
1. (a) Yosemite National Park: ecosystem boundaries are the (artificial) boundaries of the park.
   (b) The clearing's border is the edge of the grass clearing where forest trees grow again.
   (c) The tree ecosystem borders are the tree and soil and air immediately around it.

150. Habitats (page 221)
1. An organism will occupy habitat according to its range of tolerance for a particular suite of physical and biotic conditions. Organisms will tend to occupy those regions where all or most of their requirements are met and will avoid those regions where they are not. **Note:** Sometimes, a single factor, e.g. pH for an aquatic organism, will limit occupation of an otherwise suitable habitat.

2. (a) Most of a species population is found in the optimum range because this is where conditions for that species are best; most of the population will select that zone.
   (b) The greatest constraint on an organism's growth within its optimum range would be competition between it and members of the same species (or perhaps different species with similar niche requirements).

3. In a marginal habitat, the following might apply:
   – Physicochemical conditions (e.g. temperature, current speed, pH, salinity) might be sub-optimal and create stress (therefore greater vulnerability to disease).

– Food might be more scarce or of lower quality/nutritional value.
– Mates might be harder to find.
– The area might be more exposed to predators.
– Resting, sleeping, or nesting places might be harder to find and/or less suitable in terms of shelter or safety.
– Competition from other better-adapted species might be more intense.

151. Food Chains (page 222)
1. (a) Refer to the diagram, below

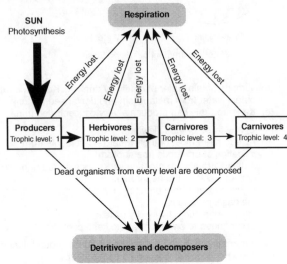

   (b) The sun.
   (c) The energy is converted to biomass through the process of photosynthesis.

2. Energy is transferred in the chemical bonds in biomass.

3. **Note** (first printing only): Students should understand that detritivores and saprotrophs (saprobionts) are consumers with specific feeding modes. Examples of these groups have been added to the photo captions for subsequent printings.

   (a) Producers: Obtain energy from the sun via photosynthesis, e.g. green plants, algae, autotrophic bacteria.
   (b) Consumers; Obtain energy by eating other organisms, e.g. animals.
   (c) Detritivores: Obtain energy from eating dead organic matter, e.g. some animals (earthworms, millipedes).
   (d) Saprotrophs: Obtain energy by extracellular digestion of dead material, e.g. fungi, decomposing bacteria.

152. Food Webs (page 223)
1. (a) Carnivore   (d) Autotroph
   (b) Detritivore   (e) Herbivore (when young)
   (c) Detritus

2. Most energy is lost from the system as heat, so very little is transferred to the next level. After six links there is very little energy left in the system (not enough energy available to support the organisms in another level).

153. Ecological Pyramids (page 224)
1. (a) Number pyramid: Numbers of individual organisms at each trophic level.
   (b) Biomass pyramid: Weight (usually dry weight) of all organisms at each trophic level.
   (c) Energy pyramid: Energy content of all organisms at each trophic level.

2. Biomass or energy pyramids usually more accurately reflect the energy available to the next trophic level than pyramids of numbers. Pyramids of numbers can be misleading because a small number of producers may represent a large amount of

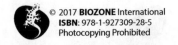

© 2017 **BIOZONE** International
ISBN: 978-1-927309-28-5
Photocopying Prohibited

biomass or energy.

3. Producers include the large trees. These have a large biomass and energy content per individual.

4. (a) 8690 → 142 = 8548 kJ = 1.6%
   (b) 142 → 12 = 130 kJ = 8.5%
   (c) Energy passed on from producers to primary consumers is less than the expected 10% because a lot of energy is diverted to the decomposers.
   (d) Decomposers.
   (e) In a plankton community, turnover times (the generation times of organisms) are very short and there is a lot of dead material in the water column and on the bottom. This provides a rich energy source to support a large decomposer biomass.

5. The algae are reproducing at a rapid rate, but are being heavily cropped by the larger zooplankton biomass.

154. Measuring Distribution and Abundance
(page 226)

1. Distribution describes the location of individuals of a species in an area. Abundance is how many of a species there are.

2. (a) Quadrat sampling
   (b) Belt transect
   (c) Area sampling

3. Information about the physical environment can help explain the distribution and abundance of the species being sampled.

4. 23 ÷ 100 x 100 = 23%. This is slightly more than was estimated using the quadrat divided into squares.

155. Quadrat Sampling (page 228)

1. Mean number of centipedes captured per quadrat:
   Total number centipedes ÷ total number quadrats
   30 individuals ÷ 37 quadrats
   = 0.811 centipedes per quadrat

2. Number per quadrat ÷ area of each quadrat
   0.811 ÷ 0.08 = 10.1 centipedes per m²

3. Clumped or random distribution.

4. Presence of suitable microhabitats for cover (e.g. logs, stones, leaf litter) may be scattered.

156. Quadrat-Based Estimates (page 229)

1. Species abundance in plant communities can be determined by using quadrats and transects, and abundance scales and percentage cover are often appropriate. Methods for sampling animal communities are more diverse and density is a more common measure of abundance.

2. **Size**: Quadrat must be large enough to be representative and small enough to minimise the amount of sampling effort.

3. **Habitat heterogeneity**: Diverse habitats require more samples to be representative because they are not homogeneous.

4. (a) and (b) any two of:
   − The values assigned to species on the abundance scale are subjective and may not be consistent between users.
   − An abundance scale may miss rarer species and overestimate conspicuous ones.
   − The scale may be inappropriate for some habitats.
   − The semi-quantitative values assigned to the abundance categories cover a range so results will lack precision.

157. Transect Sampling (page 230)

1. (a) With belt transects of 10 m or more, sampling and analysis using this method is very time consuming and labour intensive.
   (b) Line transects may not be representative of the community. There may be species which are present but which do not touch the line and are not recorded.
   (c) Belt transects use a wider strip along the study area so there is less chance that a species will not be recorded.
   (d) Transect sampling is not a suitable technique when the

species of interest are highly mobile.

2. Decrease the sampling interval. If no more species are detected and the trends along the transect remain the same, then the sampling interval was adequate.

3.

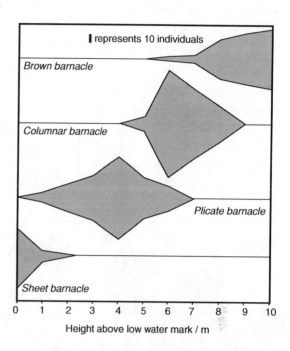

158. Qualitative Practical Work: Seaweed Zonation
(page 232)

1. (a) Percentage cover of each seaweed species.
   (b) Seaweed vigour and degree of dessication.

2. Column graph as below:

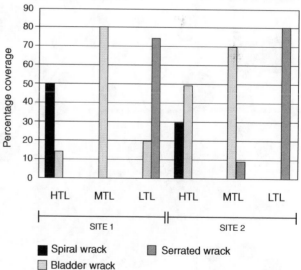

3. Spiral wrack is the most tolerant of long exposure periods, where it grows vigorously despite showing some evidence of desiccation. Bladder wrack grows vigorously throughout the midlittoral and is relatively tolerant of exposure, only showing signs of desiccation higher on the shore where exposure time is longer. Serrated wrack is intolerant of exposure and grows vigorously at the LTL but shows signs of desiccation above this and cannot compete with the more tolerant bladder wrack.

4. Quadrat position was staggered for the two sites to give a better indication of the extent of each species' distribution. The disadvantage is that the sites cannot be directly compared.

159. Sampling Techniques and Population Estimates
(page 233)

Results are given for column B of the random number table. These results are typical but results for quadrats and transects will vary depending on the random number column chosen and how the transects are drawn.

Table 1: Quadrat count

Coordinates (R:C)	Plant 1	Plant 2	Plant 3	Plant 4	Plant 5
1: 3,1	0	0	3	2	0
2: 1,5	0	2	0	3	0
3: 5,6	0	0	0	0	2
4: 3,6	0	0	0	7	0
5: 4,2	3	0	0	0	0
6: 1,4	1	0	0	3	0
TOTAL	4	2	3	15	2

Table 2: Percentage cover

Coordinates	Plant 1	Plant 2	Plant 3	Plant 4	Plant 5
1: 3,1	0	0	21	2.7	0
2: 1,5	0	37.8	0	4	0
3: 5,6	0	0	0	0.7	0.11
4: 3,6	0	0	0	8.7	0
5: 4,2	60.4	0	0	0	0
6: 1,4	22	0	0	3.2	0
MEAN %	13.9	6.3	3.5	3.2	1.8

Transects based on the B column of random numbers were drawn as below. Plants were recorded at 1 cm intervals along each transect. The quadrats for the B column of random numbers are indicated by heavier lines.

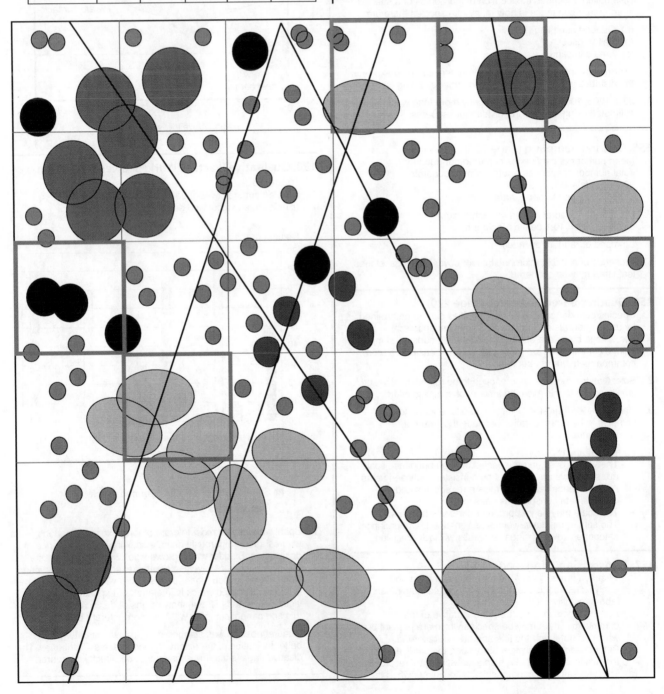

© 2017 **BIOZONE** International
ISBN: 978-1-927309-28-5
Photocopying Prohibited

Table 3: Line transect

Plant	Tally plant species	Total number	Relative abundance / %
1	IIII IIII II	12	36.4
2	IIII IIII	10	30.3
3	III	3	9.1
4	IIII I	6	18.2
5	II	2	6.0

1. (a) Plant 1: 740 m^{-2} (b) Plant 1: 15.3%
    Plant 2: 370 m^{-2} Plant 2: 7.7%
    Plant 3: 555.5 m^{-2} Plant 3: 11.5%
    Plant 4: 2778 m^{-2} Plant 4: 57.7%
    Plant 5: 370 m^{-2} Plant 5: 7.7%

2. From table: Plant 1: 13.9%, Plant 2: 6.3%, Plant 3: 3.5%,
    Plant 4: 3.2%, Plant 5: 1.8%
    Note: Figures will depend on subjective assessment of the amount of each plant is within the square. Overlapping plants of the same species will have a reduced percentage cover.

3. From table: Plant 1: 36.4%, Plant 2: 30.3%, Plant 3: 9.1%, Plant 4: 18.2%, Plant 5: 6.0%

4. Calculations on complete direct count.
    (a) Plant 1: 14 ÷ 0.0324 = 432 m^{-2}
        Plant 2: 10 ÷ 0.0324 = 308.6 m^{-2}
        Plant 3: 9 ÷ 0.0324 = 277.8 m^{-2}
        Plant 4: 110 ÷ 0.0324 = 3395 m^{-2}
        Plant 5: 9 ÷ 0.0324 = 277.8 m^{-2}
    (b) The estimates overestimated the density of plant 1 (large cover), overestimated the rarer plant 3, and were quite close (percentage-wise) for plant 4 (numerous). Note that the statement you make here will depend on your estimates in question 1(a), which will vary depending on the random number column chosen.
    (c) Plant 1: 14 ÷ 152 x 100 = 9.2%
        Plant 2: 10 ÷ 152 x 100 = 6.6%
        Plant 3: 9 ÷ 152 x 100 = 5.9%
        Plant 4: 110 ÷ 152 x 100 = 72.4%
        Plant 5: 9 ÷ 152 x 100 = 5.9%
    (d) Typographical error (first printing only). Question should read "Compare your estimated population abundance calculations to the actual population **abundance** for each species". Our apologies for any confusion

        The sampling overestimated the density of the largest plant 1 and the rarer plant 3, and underestimated the abundance of the small numerous plant 4.

5. Using a small number of quadrats tended to over-estimate the density and abundance of larger and/or rarer plants and under-estimate smaller numerous plants. The transect greatly underestimated relative abundance of smaller plants as many were missed and it greatly overestimated the relative abundance of larger plants (plants 1 and 2), which were 'hit' many times. Transects were quite accurate for medium sized plants with a clumped distribution (plant 5). Generally sampling may provide a poor estimate for rarer, larger plants or plants that are distributed unevenly in the environment, if not many samples are taken. Combining the sampling results of groups using different coordinates could correct for patchy distributions but this represents increased sampling effort. This shows the importance of selecting the right sized quadrat or the right sized sampling interval if using transects.

160. Quantifying Variation Using Student's *t* Test
(page 236)

1. (a) The calculated *t* value is less than the critical value of $t = 2.57$. The null hypothesis cannot be rejected. There is no difference between control and experimental treatments.
    (b) The new *t* value supports the alternative hypothesis at $P = 0.05$ (reject the null hypothesis and conclude that there is a difference between the control and experimental treatments). Note the critical value of *t* in this case is 2.23 at 10 d.f. $P = 0.05$

2. Statistical significance refers to the probability that an observed difference (or trend) will occur by chance. It is an arbitrary criterion used as the basis for accepting or rejecting the null hypothesis in an investigation. **Note**: In science the term 'significantly different' has a specific meaning. It should not be used in a casual manner when no statistical test has been performed.

3. Step 1: H$_0$ there is no difference in heart rate between males and females. Step 2: Test two tailed.

    (a) Completed table:

x (bpm)		x − x̄ (deviation from mean)		(x − x̄)^2 (deviation from mean)^2	
Male	**Female**	**Male**	**Female**	**Male**	**Female**
70	69	-2.3	1	5.29	1
74	62	1.7	-6	2.89	36
80	75	7.7	7	59.29	49
73	66	0.7	-2	0.49	4
75	68	2.7	0	7.29	0
82	57	9.7	-11	94.09	121
62	61	-10.3	-7	106.09	49
69	84	-3.3	16	10.89	256
70	61	-2.3	-7	5.29	49
68	77	-4.3	9	18.49	81
$n_A = 10$	$n_B = 10$			$\Sigma(x - \bar{x})^2$ 310.1	$\Sigma(x - \bar{x})^2$ 646

    (b) Variance of males: 34.45
        Variance of females: 71.78
    (c) Difference between groups means: 4.3
    (d) $t = 1.32$
    (e) Degrees of freedom: 18
    (f) $P = 0.05$, *t* (critical value) = 2.101
    (g) **Decision**: We cannot reject the null hypothesis; the difference between the two groups means is not significantly different at $P = 0.05$.

161. Quantitative Investigation of Variation (page 238)

x length / mm		x − x̄ (deviation from the mean)		(x − x̄)² (deviation from mean)²	
Paddock A	Paddock B	Paddock A	Paddock B	Paddock A	Paddock B
83	30	40.2	-77.5	1616.04	6006.25
70	87	27.2	-20.5	739.84	420.25
32	48	-10.8	-59.9	116.8	3543.1
61	92	18.2	-15.5	330.9	241.0
70	54	27.2	-53.5	739.3	2864.8
45	33	2.2	-74.5	4.8	5553.8
28	135	-14.8	27.5	219.3	754.9
34	60	-8.8	-47.5	77.6	2258.5
37	81	-5.8	-26.5	33.8	703.5
20	139	-33.8	31.5	520.3	990.8
25	90	-17.8	-17.5	317.2	307.1
30	78	-12.8	29.5	164.1	871.7
31	125	-11.8	17.5	139.5	305.4
35	174	-7.8	66.5	61.0	4419.1
80	167	37.2	59.5	1383.1	3537.4
22	184	-20.8	76.5	433.0	5848.6
62	80	19.2	-27.5	368.3	757.6
35	125	-7.8	17.5	61.0	305.4
25	163	-17.8	55.5	317.2	3077.6
44	197	1.2	89.5	1.4	8006.0
30	116	12.8	8.5	164.1	71.8

$n_A = 21$ $n_B = 21$

$\Sigma(x − x̄)^2$: 7807.2   50 849.2

Step 1

Population A: $x̄_A = 42.8$ n = 21 $s_A = 19.76$

Population B: $x̄_B = 107.5$ n = 21 $s_B = 50.4$

Step 2
Null hypothesis: There is no difference between the length of the clover stem in paddock A and paddock B

Step 3
Test is two tailed.

1. Variance population A = 390.45
   Variance population B = 2540.16

2. Difference between population means: -64.7

3. $t = -64.7/ \sqrt{((390.45/21) + 2540.16/21))} = -5.48$

4. d.f = 21 + 21 -2 = 40

5. P = 0.01 $t = 2.704$

6. 5.48 exceeds 2.704 so we can reject the null hypothesis.

7. There is a significant difference between the length of the clover stems in paddock A and B.

8. Clover in paddocks A and B would need to be cut, dried, and weighed under the same 'cropping' regime. Therefore instead of using cattle, a mower with a catcher would need to used.

162. Pearson's Linear Correlation (page 240)

1.

x	y	(x-x̄)²	y-ȳ)²	xy
36.21	19.75	7993.72	4.90	715.15
33.76	17.53	8437.82	0.00	591.81
10.83	15.05	13176.19	6.18	162.99
1.88	14.40	15310.99	9.83	27.07
0.33	11.73	15696.98	33.71	3.87
2.40	11.05	15182.58	42.07	26.52
0.35	9.23	15691.97	68.99	3.23
0.08	8.75	15759.69	77.19	0.70
0.00	12.35	15779.78	26.89	0.00
0.04	13.13	15769.73	19.41	0.53
0.00	14.15	15779.78	11.46	0.00
0.21	14.63	15727.07	8.44	3.07
0.29	15.98	15707.01	2.42	4.63
5.72	19.63	14375.43	4.38	112.28
4.39	18.00	14696.13	0.22	79.02
7.42	19.80	13970.67	5.13	146.92
72.87	23.33	2782.31	33.57	1700.06
443.38	23.30	100972.94	33.22	10330.75
34.38	22.30	8324.30	22.70	766.67
147.58	25.88	482.35	69.62	3819.37
947.64	24.58	675720.83	49.62	23292.99
573.47	22.90	200571.77	28.77	13132.46
444.63	20.95	101768.91	11.66	9315.00
338.25	21.10	45212.54	12.70	7137.08
34.33	18.90	8333.43	1.86	648.84
x̄= 125.62	ȳ=17.54	Σ(x - x̄)² = 1373224.92	Σ(y - y)² = 584.96	Σxy = 72021.02
s_x= 234.4	s_y= 4.8		r = 0.60	

2. An r of 0.60 tells us that there is a reasonably strong positive correlation between the temperature of the pond water and the number of *Hexarthra* present.

© 2017 **BIOZONE** International
ISBN: 978-1-927309-28-5
Photocopying Prohibited

163. Spearman Rank Correlation (page 241)

1. H_0: There is no correlation between the number of plant species and the volume of precipitation (rainfall).

2. (a) 0.5875 (b) Positive (c) Significant

Site	R_1	R_2	$D (R_1-R_2)$	D^2
1	12	15	-3	9
2	14	14	0	0
3	15	13	2	4
4	11	12	-1	1
5	10	11	-1	1
6	13	9	4	16
7	7	4.5	2.5	6.25
8	6	7.5	-1.5	2.25
9	8	3	5	25
10	5	6	-1	1
11	4	2	2	4
12	9	1	8	64
13	3	10	-7	49
14	2	4.5	-2.5	6.25
15	1	7.5	-6.5	42.25
			$\Sigma D^2 =$	231

$$r_s \text{ value} = 1 - (6 \times 231) \div (15^3 - 15)$$
$$= 1 - (1386 \div 3360)$$
$$= 1 - 0.4125 = 0.5875$$

164. What is Primary Productivity? (page 242)

1. Estuaries, swamps, and tropical rainforests typically have higher temperatures (than open water or temperate forest), ample water, and readily available nitrogen thus yielding higher net productivities.

2. (a) [initial - dark] = 8 mg O_2 L^{-1} - 5 mg O_2 L^{-1} = 3 mg O_2 L^{-1}
   (b) [light - initial] = 10 mg O_2 L^{-1} - 8 mg O_2 L^{-1} = 2 mg O_2 L^{-1}
   (c) [light - dark] = 10 mg O_2 L^{-1} - 5 mg O_2 L^{-1} = 5 mg O_2 L^{-1}
      (or NPP + R = 2 mg O_2 L^{-1} + 3 mg O_2 L^{-1} = 5 mg O_2 L^{-1})
   (d) 9.4 grams of glucose ÷ 2 = 4.7 grams of glucose

165. Productivity and Trophic Efficiency (page 243)

1. (a)- (c) and any of the following:
   - Amount and availability of light for photosynthesis. This is higher in the tropics.
   - Temperature. Higher temperatures are generally associated with higher productivity.
   - Availability of water. Photosynthesis (and therefore productivity) will be limited when water is scarce.
   - Availability of nutrients. Nutrient limitations will limit plant growth and lower productivity.

2. (a) Secondary productivity is the rate of production of consumer biomass.
   (b) High palatability and turnover of biomass contribute to high secondary productivity. The large number of trophic connections also reduce energy losses within the system.

166. Energy Inputs and Outputs (page 244)

1. (a) Metabolic wastes as urine, faeces, and carbon dioxide.
   (b) Heat as a result of cellular metabolism

2. (a) Corn: 138.0 ÷ 8548 X 100 = 1.61 %
      Pasture: 24.4 ÷ 1971 x 100 = 1.24 %
   (b) Corn: 32.2 ÷ 138.0 x 100 = 23.3%
      Pasture: 3.7 ÷ 24.4 x 100 = 15.2%
   (c) Corn: 105 ÷ 138 x 100 = 76.7%
      Pasture: 20.7 ÷ 24.4 x 100 = 84.8%
   (d) The mature pasture

3. If N = 20% of I (700 kJ), then N = 0.2 x 700 = 140.
   Energy lost as F and R =700 – 140 = 560 kJ.

4. See percent biomass column in table below

5. See Energy columns in table below

6. See NPP column in table below

Age in days	Percent biomass	Energy in 10 plants / kJ	Energy per plant / kJ	NPP / kJ plant^{-1} d^{-1}
7	21.4	76.4	7.6	1.09
14	24.2	169.3	16.9	1.2
21	28.1	282.1	28.2	1.34

7. Transfer NPP figures above to the first column of Table 2. Mean calculation below:

Age in days	Mean NPP / kJ plant^{-1} d^{-1}
7	1.09
14	1.21
21	1.34

8.

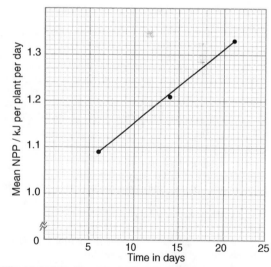

9. (a) NPP increases over time in a linear fashion.
   (b) NPP increases over time because anabolic processes in the plants increase the amount of plant tissue that can be used both to capture more of the sun's energy and as energy for the next trophic level (e.g. more sugars, more cellulose, more chlorophyll).

10. To determine the GPP of *B. rapa* you would need to know how much energy the plants have lost in respiration.

11. A basic methodology as follows:

   Introduction:

   Of the NPP from the brussels sprouts that is consumed by the caterpillars, some will be used in cellular respiration, some will be available to secondary consumers (the net 2° production)

© 2017 **BIOZONE** International
ISBN: 978-1-927309-28-5
Photocopying Prohibited

and some will be lost as waste products (frass).

Note that in the energy values provided in the activity, plant mass contains different percentages of organic compounds to animal material and frass. Different organic compounds contain different amounts of energy per gram.

Method

- Put a small amount of brussels sprouts in an aerated container with 10, 12 day old caterpillars. Weigh the brussels sprouts and the caterpillars to obtain a wet mass.

- After 3 days, disassemble the container and record the mass of the remaining brussels sprouts, caterpillars, and frass.

- In separate containers, dry the remaining brussels sprouts, the caterpillars, and the frass in a drying oven to obtain the dry mass.

- For brussels sprouts tabulate:
  (a) Wet mass on days 1 and 3
  (b) Dry mass on day 3 (after drying)

- On the table for brussels sprouts calculate:
  (c) Percent biomass on day 3 (dry÷wet x 100). Assume percent biomass on day 1 is the same.
  (d) Plant energy on days 1 and 3 (wet mass x percent biomass x 18.2 kJ)
  (e) Plant energy eaten per caterpillar in 3 days (plant energy day 1 – plant energy day 3 ÷ 10 caterpillars)

Assumptions: That the percent biomass of brussels sprouts (and caterpillars) on day 1 is the same as the calculated value from day 3. You cannot calculate percent biomass on day 1 because it would mean destroying the food and the caterpillars.

- For caterpillars tabulate:
  (f) Wet mass on days 1 and 3 and mass gained (g)
  (g) Wet mass per individual on days 1 and 3 and mass gained (g) (mass gained ÷ 10)
  (h) Dry mass on day 3 (after drying)

- On the table for caterpillars calculate:
  (i) Caterpillar percent biomass on day 3 (dry÷wet x 100). Assume percent biomass on day 1 is the same.
  (j) **Net secondary production**
  Energy production per caterpillar on days 1 and 3 (individual wet mass x percent biomass x 23.0 kJ). Net secondary production = kJ gained per caterpillar = Energy production per caterpillar day 3 – day 1
  (k) **Efficiency of energy transfer, producers to consumers**: Energy production per caterpillar day 3 – energy production per caterpillar day 1 (j) ÷ plant energy eaten per caterpillar (e) x 100 should be ~10% (or less)

- For frass tabulate:
  (l) Dry mass of frass from 10 caterpillars

- On the table for frass calculate:
  (m) Frass energy = frass dry mass x 19.87 kJ
  (n) Energy of frass from 1 caterpillar (frass energy ÷ 10)

To calculate respiratory losses:
Plant energy eaten per caterpillar (e)
minus Energy production per caterpillar (net 2° production) (j)
minus Frass energy per caterpillar (n)

---

167. Energy Budget in an Ecosystem (page 246)

1. (a) 14 000 (c) 35
   (b) 180   (d) 100

2. Solar energy

3. A. Photosynthesis
   B. Eating/feeding/ingestion
   C. Respiration
   D. Export (lost from this ecosystem to another)
   E. Decomposers and detritivores feeding on other decomposers and detritivores
   F. Radiation of heat to the atmosphere
   G. Excretion/egestion/death

4. (a) 1 700 000 ÷ 7 000 000 x 100 = 24.28%

(b) It is reflected. **Note**: Plants appear green because those wavelengths are not absorbed. Reflected light falls on other objects as well as back into space.

5. (a) 87 400 ÷ 1 700 000 x 100 = 5.14%
   (b) 1 700 000 - 87 400 = 1 612 600 (94.86%)
   (c) Most of the energy absorbed by producers is not used in photosynthesis. This excess energy, which is not fixed, is lost as heat (although the heat loss component before the producer level is not usually shown on energy flow diagrams). **Note**: Some of the light energy absorbed through accessory pigments such as carotenoids widens the spectrum that can drive photosynthesis. However, much of accessory pigment activity is associated with photoprotection; they absorb and dissipate excess light energy that would otherwise damage chlorophyll.

6. (a) 78 835 kJ
   (b) 78 835 ÷ 1 700 000 x 100 = 4.64%

7. (a) Decomposers and detritivores
   (b) Transport by wind or water to another ecosystem (e.g. blown or carried in water currents).

8. (a) Low oxygen or anaerobic, low temperature, low moisture.
   (b) Energy remains locked up in the detrital material and is not released.
   (c) Geological reservoir:

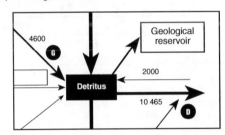

   (d) See the carbon cycle activity. Fossil fuels such as oil, natural gas, and coal. Oil (petroleum) and natural gas are formed from the remains of marine plankton. Coal and peat are both of plant origin; peat is partly decomposed, and coal is fossilised.

9. (a) 87 400 → 14 000: 14 000 ÷ 87 400 x 100 = 16%
   (b) 14 000 → 1600: 1600 ÷14 000 x 100 = 11.4%
   (c) 1600 → 90: 90 ÷ 1600 x 100 = 5.6
   (d) Producers to primary consumers

---

168. Nutrient Cycles (page 248)

1. (a) Bacteria are able to make conversions to and from elements and their ionic states. This gives plants and animals access to nutrients that they would otherwise not have (i.e. increases bioavailability).
   (b) Fungi decompose organic matter, returning nutrients to the soil where plants and bacteria can access them. They are also able to convert some nutrients into more readily accessible forms.
   (c) Plants are able make their own food and, when they die, add this to the soil in the form of nutrients that can be broken down and used by bacteria and fungi. They also provide browsing animals with nutrients when they are eaten.
   (d) Animals break down materials from plants, fungi and bacteria and return then to the soil with their wastes and when they die allowing the nutrients in them to re-enter the cycle.

2. The rates of decomposition are very high in the higher temperatures of tropical forests. As a result, decaying matter is processed very quickly and very little remains in the soil. Much of the carbon and other nutrients are also locked up in biomass.

3. A macronutrient is one that is required in large amounts. Micronutrients (also called trace elements) are needed in much smaller amounts.

© 2017 **BIOZONE** International
ISBN: 978-1-927309-28-5
Photocopying Prohibited

169. The Nitrogen Cycle (page 249)

1. (a)-(e) any of:
   - Decomposition or decay of dead organisms, to ammonia by decomposer bacteria (ammonification).
   - Nitrification of ammonium ions to nitrite by nitrifying bacteria such as *Nitrosomonas* ($NH_4^+ \rightarrow NO_2^-$)
   - Nitrification of nitrite to nitrate by nitrifying bacteria such as *Nitrobacter* ($NO_2^- \rightarrow NO_3^-$)
   - Denitrification of nitrate to nitrogen gas by anaerobic denitrifying bacteria such as *Pseudomonas* ($NO_3^- \rightarrow N_{2(g)}$)
   - Fixation of atmospheric nitrogen to nitrate by nitrogen fixing bacteria such as *Azotobacter* and *Rhizobium* ($N_2 \rightarrow NO_3^-$)
   - Fixation of atmospheric nitrogen to ammonia by nitrogen fixing cyanobacteria ($N_2 \rightarrow NH_3$)

2. (a) Oxidation of atmospheric nitrogen by lightning.
   (b) Nitrogen fixation (by bacteria).
   (c) Production of nitrogen fertiliser by the Haber process.

3. Denitrification.

4. The atmosphere.

5. Nitrate.

6. Any one of: Amino acids, proteins, chlorophyll.

7. Animals obtain their nitrogen by ingesting (eating) food (plants or other animals).

8. Leguminous material is high in nitrogen. Ploughing it in replenishes soil nitrogen and reduces the need for additional nitrogen fertiliser when growing non-leguminous crops subsequently.

9. (a)-(e) any five in any order:
   - Addition of nitrogen fertilisers to the land. This supplies inorganic nitrogen, as nitrate, for plant growth, but excess nitrogen, not absorbed by plants, may enter and pollute water sources.
   - Industrial physical-chemical fixation of nitrogen (through the Haber process) combines H and N to ammonia, which can be used to manufacture inorganic nitrogen fertilisers. This is an industrial process, requiring high temperatures and pressures and a large amount of energy. The effects of applied inorganic nitrogen are outlined above.
   - Genetic modification of plants so that they can fix nitrogen. The effect of this is to increase the range of crop plants capable of growing on nitrogen deficient soils. Potentially, this could make a beneficial contribution to soil fertility.
   - Large-scale, assisted composting produces nitrogen rich organic fertiliser which has the effect of improving soil fertility and structure. This has beneficial effects in reducing the amount of inorganic nitrogen fertiliser that must be applied for the desired plant growth.
   - Burning and harvesting removes nitrogen from the land and releases nitrogen oxides into the air.
   - Discharge of effluent (particular animal waste) into waterways enriches water bodies and leads to localised pollution and eutrophication.
   - Irrigation can accelerate loss of nitrate from the soil by increasing the rate at which nitrates are washed out of the soil into ground water.

170. The Carbon Cycle (page 251)

1. Arrows can be added as on the diagram below (white arrows) for the points (a)-(d) as follows:
   (a) Dissolving of limestone by acid rain: Arrow from the limestone layer to atmospheric CO_2.
   (b) Release of carbon from the marine food chain: Arrows (labelled **respiration**) from marine organisms to atmospheric CO_2.
   (c) Mining and burning of coal: Arrow from the coal seam to atmospheric CO_2.
   (d) Burning of plant material: Arrow (labelled **combustion**) from the trees and/or grassland to atmospheric CO_2.

2. (a) **Respiration** (stepwise oxidation of glucose) and **combustion** (rapid oxidation of organic substances).

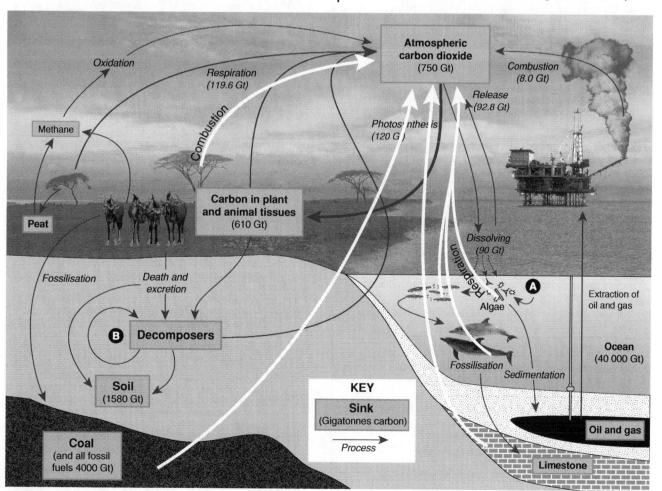

(b) Both involve the release of CO_2.

3. (a) - (d) in any order:
Atmosphere; coal; limestone; oil and natural gas.

4. (a) Photosynthesis   (b) Respiration

5. There would be no decomposition and carbon would eventually be locked up in the bodies (remains) of dead organisms. Possible gradual loss of CO_2 from the atmosphere.

6. (a) Coal: Plant material trapped under sediment in swampy conditions millions of years ago.
(b) Oil: Marine plankton rapidly buried in sediment mya.
(c) Limestone (also chalk = fine limestone): Shells of molluscs, skeletons of coral and other marine organisms with skeletons of calcium carbonate piled upon seabeds and compressed.
(d) Peat: Partly decayed vegetation formed because of acidic or anaerobic conditions.

7. Producers use CO_2 as the raw material to produce organic compounds via photosynthesis. Consumers use these as food and incorporate the carbon into their own bodies. During respiration, all organisms transfer the energy in organic compounds to ATP and release CO_2 into the atmosphere. When organisms die, decomposition returns carbon to the carbon pool. The carbon that is not utilised by decomposers may be incorporated into fossil fuels or other carbon sinks.

8. (a) Humans deplete the carbon stored in sinks through extraction and combustion of fossil fuels.
(b) Human activity has resulted in an increase in atmospheric levels of carbon dioxide.

---

171. Ecosystems Are Dynamic (page 253)
1. A dynamic system is one that is constantly changing. Ecosystems, although they may appear constant are continually changing in response to changes in the weather and seasons and the activities of the organisms in them.

2. (a) Any two of: fire, flood, seasonal drought, landslides.
(b) Open pit mining, large scale forest clearance, volcanic eruptions, inundation caused by sea level rise, prolonged drought (desert formation) as caused by climate shifts.

3. A climax community is one that apparently remains the same over time (there is no succession to a different community). However, an ecosystem is constantly changing. In a climax community, an equilibrium exists between growth and death in the community so that it appears static over the long term.

---

172. Ecosystem Changes (page 254)
1. (a) When dry, peat is used as a fuel source.
(b) Peat forms very slowly and removing it destroys the system and the conditions that maintained it. It may take hundreds or thousands of years for a mined peat bog to recover (if ever).
(c) Mining below the water table creates a lake (open water) ecosystem, which are vastly different to the peat bog that was there before. The lake removes any chance of the peat bog recovering and also meant the land was no longer available for agriculture.

2. Loss of the fir, cedar, and pine forests, which were replaced by volcanic ash.

3. This area was closest to the volcanic blast and consequently suffered the largest amount of damage. Its altitude and covering of volcanic ash make it difficult for plants to reestablish there.

4. Coldwater Creek was blocked, forming Coldwater lake, changing the system from flowing water to static water.

5. Spirit lake was completely emptied and all life, except bacteria, was killed. When the refilled lake recovers, its new community will reestablish under quite different conditions and its characteristics are likely to be quite different.

6. (a) The river now originates at the crater instead of Spirit Lake and it is now heavily laden with sediment.
(b) The original community was adapted to a clear water environment. The river is now laden with sediment and the community will change to one that is tolerant of the different conditions. Species that depend on clear water will disappear.

---

173. Primary Succession (page 256)
1. Glacial retreat, exposed slip, new volcanic island.

2. (a) Lichens, mosses, liverworts, and hardy annual herb species are often the first to colonise bare ground.
(b) (i) Chemically and physically erode rock (producing the beginnings of a soil). (ii) Add nutrients by decay.

3. Climax communities tend to have higher biodiversity and a more complex trophic structure than early successional communities. A greater diversity of community interactions buffers the system against disturbances because there are many more organisms with different ecological roles able to compensate for losses from the system.

---

174. Succession on Surtsey Island (page 257)
1. Surtsey was ideal as a study site for primary succession because it was an entirely new island, devoid of any soil, and was isolated from nearby influences (such as already established vegetation or urban settlements) that could accelerate the succession process.

2. Early colonisations were the result of seeds blown from Iceland to the Northern shore, which is the closest shore. Later colonisations were in the south due to the establishment of the gull colony. The gulls would transport seeds and contribute to soil fertility.

3. (a) 1985.
(b) Transported by birds.
(c) 1985. This coincides with the establishment of the gull colony as the gulls were instrumental in dispersing seeds.

---

175. Secondary Succession (page 258)
1. Primary succession refers to the colonisation of regions where there is no preexisting community (e.g. new volcanic island). Changes in the community occur in stages until a climax community is reached. Secondary succession follows the interruption of an established climax community (e.g. logging, pasture reverting to forest).

2. Secondary succession proceeds more rapidly than primary succession because although the land is cleared, there is minimal or no loss of soil or seed stores. Many plants may still be able to grow despite the disturbance and the climax community will reestablish faster because nutrients are already available and seeds already laid down.

3. Any one example: Events that result in secondary succession include forest fires, minor landslides, storm or cyclonic damage, the fall of a canopy tree, flooding, or human induced land clearance.

4. (a) Removal of trees clears the land of the existing vegetation and allows species typical of an earlier successional stage (sere) to establish and occupy the cleared region.
(b) Selective logging would result in a gap regeneration succession because it would mimic the natural process of a tree falling in the forest followed by the rapid growth of young canopy trees to occupy the space.
(c) Selective logging is considered to be less damaging to an existing ecosystem because there is still a favourable environment in which seedlings can mature. Canopy gaps are created naturally by windfalls and selective logging could be said to mimic this, so the gaps created may be beneficial for forest diversity and regeneration.

5. (a) A deflected succession refers to a succession that is deflected from its natural course by human intervention. The plagioclimax that develops is different from the one that would have developed if there had been no intervention.
(b) A deflected succession keeps the managed habitat as a modified environment in a certain state. Many human-modified landscapes (e.g. farm lands) are managed (by burning, grazing, mowing) with the express purpose

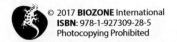© 2017 **BIOZONE** International
ISBN: 978-1-927309-28-5
Photocopying Prohibited

of preventing the establishment of a natural climax community. These communities are distinct from those that would naturally develop if the land were left alone.

---

176. Population Size and Carrying Capacity (page 260)

1. The carrying capacity is the maximum number of individuals of a particular species that an environment can support indefinitely.

2. The carrying capacity is set by the resources it can provide and these are limited. If a population increases above the carrying capacity, there will be insufficient resources to sustain it, and the population will decrease (e.g. through deaths) to a level that can be supported by the available resources.

3. (a) 3: Food and space have been reduced.
   (b) 5; Available water (and consequently food) are reduced due to the drought.
   (c) 6: Water is more available.

---

177. A Case Study in Carrying Capacity (page 261)

1. Wolves were introduced to control the black-tailed deer, which were overgrazing the land.

2. (a) Factors causing the result included:
   - Coronation Island was too small to sustain both deer and wolf populations.
   - The deer couldn't hide from the wolves so could be reduced to very low numbers.
   - Reproductive rates of deer could have been low because of poor forage, so the population could not withstand predation.
   - There were no other prey so no opportunity for prey switching when deer became scarce.
   (b) The carrying capacity of Coronation Island is too low to support viable (sustainable) populations of a large predator (wolf) and its prey (deer).

---

179. Chi-Squared Exercise in Ecology (page 263)

1. (a) H_0: "There is no difference between the numbers of periwinkles associated with different seaweed species".
   (b) H_A: "There is a real difference between the numbers of periwinkles associated with different seaweed species. Periwinkles show preference for the seaweed species with which they associate".

2. (a) Completed table:

Category	O	E	O − E	$(O − E)^2$	$\frac{(O − E)^2}{E}$
Spiral wrack	9	30	−21	441	14.70
Bladder wrack	28	30	−2	4	0.13
Toothed wrack	19	30	−11	121	4.03
Knotted wrack	64	30	34	1156	38.53
	Σ 120				Σ 57.4

   (b) $\chi^2 = 57.39$ (57.4)
   (c) Degrees of freedom = 3 (4-1)
   (d) The critical value of χ^2 at $P = 0.05$ and at d.f.= 3 is 7.82. The calculated χ^2 is (much) greater than the critical value (57.4 >> 7.82). *This means that **by chance alone**, a χ^2 value of 57.4 could be expected less than 0.1% of the time.*
   (e) Reject H_0: The data are strongly in favour of H_A. Periwinkles show significant preference for one seaweed species (knotted wrack) over the others.

3. (a) H_0: "There is no difference between the number of woodlice in each habitat; woodlice show no preference for either habitat".
   H_A: "There is a real difference between the numbers of woodlice found in dry and humid conditions".

(b) Calculation of χ^2:
   - Total no. of woodlice observed in dry = 15
   - Total no. of woodlice observed in humid = 35
   Completed table:

Category	O	E	O − E	$(O − E)^2$	$\frac{(O − E)^2}{E}$
Dry atmosphere	15	25	−10	100	4
Humid atmosphere	35	25	10	100	4
	Σ 50				Σ 8

   $\chi^2 = 8$

(c) Degrees of freedom = 1 (2-1)
   The critical value of χ^2 at $P = 0.05$ and at d.f.= 1 is 3.84. χ^2calc. > than the critical value (8 > 3.84).
(d) Reject H_0: The data are strongly in favour of H_A. Woodlice show significant preference for humid conditions over dry habitat conditions.
   Note: When dealing with only two categories (i.e. d.f. = 1) **Yate's correction** formula should be used:
   $\chi^2 = \Sigma ((O-E) - 0.5)^2 /E$
   Using on this formula, $\chi^2 = 7.22$. This is still greater than the critical value so H_0 is rejected.

---

180. Investigating Distribution and Abundance (page 264)

1.

Tree log	Distance from tree log / m			
	0	1.5	2.5	3.5
1	22	23	5	3
2	17	8	6	5
3	17	14	10	5
4	6	9	3	8
5	18	13	18	15
6	21	20	15	3
TOTAL	101	87	57	39

2. Chi-squared is a statistical test to determine the significance of departures from an expected result (in this case that there would be no difference in the number of millipedes with distance from the log). Chi-squared can be used on this data because the data are counts (not measures or calculated values) and the counts can be tested against departures from the expected result (of no difference with distance).

3. Null hypothesis: The distance from the log has no effect on the density of millipedes in the leaf litter.

   Alternative hypothesis: The distance from the log has an effect on the density of millipedes in the leaf litter.

4.

Distance / m	O	E	O-E	$(O-E)^2$	$(O-E)^2 \div E$
0	101	71	30	900	12.7
1.5	87	71	16	256	3.6
2.5	57	71	-14	196	2.7
3.5	39	71	-32	1024	14.4
				$\Sigma (O-E)^2 \div E$	33.4

5. Chi-squared is very large for this test and as such the null hypothesis can be rejected in favour of the alternative hypothesis.

6. Students had previously established that relative humidity was higher closer to the log so they could have taken a relative humidity reading at each point on the transect they sampled. This would also help to test the assumption that both

sides of log were not very different.

7. The results of the investigation significantly show that fallen logs have an effect on the distribution of millipedes in that the number of millipedes decreases with increasing distance from the log. This makes sense in relation to how millipedes live. Millipedes do not have a waterproof cuticle and thus lose water easily. Fallen logs tend to be moist underneath with an abundance of leaf litter and rotting wood, and would provide an ideal habitat for millipedes.

181. Species Interactions (page 266)

1. (a) Mutualism: Domesticated animals (e.g. dogs and cats in western culture, work horses) and plants not grown for consumption.
   (b) Exploitation: Using plants and animals for food source, skins/pelts for clothing, timber and other plant products for shelter and building materials.
   (c) Competition: Invertebrate pests and some fungi feeding on our crops (e.g. insects such as aphids, locusts, caterpillars; slugs, snails, mildew, rusts).

2. (a) Acacia produces toxic alkaloids in response to browsing.
   (b) This response makes the giraffe move on to another plant before it removes too much of the acacia's foliage.

3. (a) Mutualism
   (b) Both species benefit. Flowers are pollinated and bees gain food.

4. (a) Commensalism or perhaps mutualism
   (b) The anemone shrimp benefits by gaining protection while the anemone is (apparently) unaffected. However, there is some limited evidence that anemones may benefit although this isn't confirmed. The anemones house photosynthetic algae in their tissues that produce nutrients that are used by the anemone. These algae benefit from the ammonium released by the shrimps so indirectly, the anemone also benefits.

5. (a) Predation
   (b) The hyaena benefits while the prey is harmed (killed).

6. (a) Parasitism
   (b) The tick benefits while the host is harmed.

7. (a) Commensalism or mutualism
   (b) The egret benefits by feeding on the insects disturbed by the herbivore. The herbivore is either not affected or gains a small benefit by having annoying (and potentially disease-carrying) insects removed from the grazing area.

8. Both feed off another organism but, unlike a predator, a parasite does not kill its host.

182. Interpreting Predator-Prey Relationships (page 268)

1. (a) Peak numbers of woolly aphids and ladybird marked on graph (below).

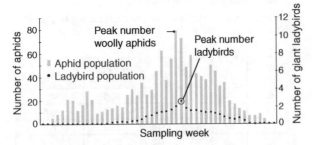

   (b) No, they are slightly offset (ladybirds lag).
   (c) Giant ladybirds feed only on woolly aphids, so ladybird numbers can only increase if there is enough food (woolly aphids) to sustain population growth. Giant ladybird numbers will respond to the woolly aphid numbers and slightly lag behind.

2. (a) Positive.
   (b) Giant ladybird numbers follow the trend for woolly aphid numbers. When woolly aphid numbers are increasing, the giant ladybird numbers increase. As woolly aphid numbers decrease so do the giant ladybird numbers.

183. Interspecific Competition (page 269)

1. The two species have similar niche requirements (similar habitats and foods). Red squirrels once occupied a much larger range than currently. This range has contracted steadily since the introduction of the greys. The circumstantial evidence points to the reds being displaced by the greys.

2. The greys have not completely displaced the reds. In areas of suitable coniferous habitat, the reds have maintained their numbers. In some places the two species coexist. **Note**: It has been suggested that the reds are primarily coniferous dwellers and extended their range into deciduous woodland habitat in the absence of competition.

3. Habitat management allows more effective long term population management *in-situ* (preferable because the genetic diversity of species is generally maintained better in the wild). Reds clearly can hold their own in competition with greys, provided they have sufficient resources. **Enhancing the habitat** preferred by the reds (through preservation and tree planting), assists their success. Providing **extra suitable food plants** also enables the reds to increase their breeding success and maintain their weight through winter (thus entering the breeding season in better condition).

4. Other conservation strategies to aid red squirrel populations could include (any of): Captive breeding and release of reds into areas where they have been displaced, control/cull of grey squirrels (particularly in habitats suitable for reds), transfer of reds from regions where populations are successful to other regions of suitable habitat, supplementary feeding prior to the breeding season, public education to encourage red squirrels over greys.

5. (a) A represents the region actually occupied by *Chthamalus*, i.e. its realised niche. **Note** (first printing only): The fundamental niche is the entire range an organism could occupy. The realised niche is range actually occupied. These terms have since been defined on the page.
   (b) When *Balanus* is removed from the lower shore, the range of *Chthalamus* extends into areas previously occupied by the *Balanus*; *Balanus* normally excludes *Chthalamus* from the lower shore.

184. Niche Differentiation (page 271)

1. (a) When resources are limited during the winter, coal tits forage in the needles and upper parts of the tree, goldcrests forage near the ground, crested tits forage in the lower parts of the tree, and blue tits forage in the middle heights of pine trees.
   (b) When other birds are absent, coal tits occupy more of the tree than when other species are present. In addition, when food resources are more abundant, the various tit species forage in more parts of the tree than in winter and more of the foraging locations overlap.

2. **Required answer**: Generally, the foraging ranges of the birds overlap during warmer months when food is more plentiful but they restrict their foraging to separate regions of the tree in winter when food is scarce. **Further explanatory detail**: When resources are more abundant, coal tits occupy more of the tree and spend more time foraging in the needles. In winter, they forage more in the upper parts of the tree. Goldcrests forage near the ground in winter but higher up the tree in warmer months. Crested tits spend much more time foraging in the lower parts of the tree during winter but will forage in every part of the tree (overlapping with other species) in warmer months. Blue tits forage in the middle parts of the tree but feed higher in the tree in winter than in summer.

185. Intraspecific Competition (page 272)

1. (a) Individual growth rate: Intraspecific competition may reduce individual growth rate when there are insufficient resources for all individuals. Examples: tadpoles, *Daphnia*, many mammals with large litters. **Note**: Individuals compete for limited resources and growth is limited in those that do not get access to sufficient food.

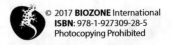

(b) Population growth rate: Intraspecific competition reduces population growth rate. Examples as above. **Note:** Competition intensifies with increasing population size and, at carrying capacity, the rate of population increase slows to zero.

(c) Final population size: Intraspecific competition will limit population size to a level that can be supported by the carrying capacity of the environment. **Note**: In territorial species, this will be determined by the number of suitable territories that can be supported.

2. (a) They reduce their individual growth rate and take longer to reach the size for metamorphosis.
   (b) Density dependent.
   (c) The results of this tank experiment are unlikely to represent a real situation because the tank tadpoles are not subject to normal sources of mortality and there is no indication of long term survival of the growth impaired tadpoles. **Note:** At high densities, many tadpoles would fail to reproduce and this would naturally limit population growth (and size) in the longer term.

3. Reduce intensity of intraspecific competition by:
   (a) Establishing hierarchies within a social group to give orderly access to resources.
   (b) Establishing territories to defend the resource within a specified area.

4. (a) Carrying capacity might decline as a result of unfavourable climatic events (drought, flood etc.) or loss of a major primary producer (plant species).
   (b) Final population size would be smaller (relative to what it was when carrying capacity was higher).

5. Territoriality is a common consequence of intraspecific competition in mammals and birds. In any habitat, resources are limited and only those with sufficient resources will be able to breed. This is especially the case with mammals and birds, where the costs of reproduction to the individual are high relative to some other taxa. Even though energy must be used in establishing and maintaining a territory, territoriality is energy efficient in the longer term because it gives the breeding pair relatively unchallenged access to resources. As is shown in the territory maps of golden eagles and great tits, territories space individuals apart and reduce intraspecific interactions. The size of the territory is related to the resources available within the defended area; larger territories are required when resources are poorer or widely dispersed. As is shown by the great tit example, when territory owners are removed, their areas are quickly occupied by birds previously displaced by competition.

186. Humans Depend on Ecosystems (page 274)

1. Ecosystem services are the benefits provided by the material or energy outputs of ecosystems. They include resources such as food and water as well as processes such as nutrient cycling, carbon storage and purification of air and water. These services are essential to human well being.

2. A healthy biodiverse ecosystem is more resilient (resistant to disturbance) and able to provide the services on which humans depend more efficiently and without degradation.

3. (a) A value can be placed on ecosystem services by estimating what people would pay for those services if they were not free, e.g. what is the commercial value of a fishery present in an area.
   (b) Placing a monetary value on ecosystem services makes it possible to estimate the costs and benefits of management options. For example, a restoration option for an ecosystem may not be viable if it was more costly than the estimated monetary value of the services provided by that ecosystem.

4. (a) RA + T_1 (resources available + technology applied) and/or T_2 technology applied would have to increase.
   (b) Technology applied (T_1) to manage resources would have to increase. (B + T_2 could increase but the aim here is to reduce resource use rather than resources being depleted).
   (c) Technology comes as at a cost (C) so costs would increase.

(d) Reducing B and RA will reduce HS if C (effort put into T_1 and T_2) doesn't change or increase C (T_1 and T_2) to keep HS at the same level.

187. Human Sustainability (page 276)

1. Almost 2%

2. At least 9.7 billion

3. (a) N = (B + I) − (D + E) where N is the population growth, D = deaths, B = births, I = immigration, and E = emigration
   (b) There would be no migration.
   (c) N = B − D

4. The human population has increased rapidly because of improvements in medicine (lower death rate) and agriculture (more food leading to higher birth rates).

5.

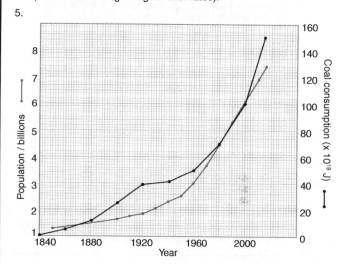

6. The curves are exponential or nearly so (the rate of coal consumption falls slightly for a short time after the end of WWI while population growth rate increases slightly over the same period).

7. (a) 70 230 + (5225 + 6556) − (4978 + 4096) = 72 937
   (b) 72 937 − 70 230 = 2707 / 70 230 = 3.85%
   (c) 4.6 x 10^7 / 70 230 = 654.99 L per person per day
   (d) 72 937 x 654.99 = 4.77 x 10^7 L
   (e) Water use calculations:
       2020: N = 75 745 x 654.99 L = 49.6 million L
       2025: N = 78 661 x 654.99 L = 51.5 million L
       2030: N = 81 690 x 654.99 L = 53.5 million L
       2035: N = 84 835 x 654.99 L = 55.6 million L
       2040: N = 88 101 x 654.99 L = 57 million L
       2045: N = 91 493 x 654.99 L = 59.9 million L
       Unsustainable between 2045 and 2050
   (f) 10% reduction in water use:
       = 0.1 x 654.99 L = 65.499 L reduction per person
       = 589.49 L per person per day. Recalculating:
       2025: N = 78 661 x 589.49 L = 46.37 million L
       2030: N = 81 690 x 589.49 L = 48.15 million L
       2035: N = 84 835 x 589.49 L = 50.00 million L
       2040: N = 88 101 x 589.49 L = 51.93 million L
       2045: N = 91 493 x 589.49 L = 53.93 million L
       2050: N = 95 015 x 589.49 L = 56.00 million L
       2055: N = 98 673 x 589.49 L = 58.17 million L
       2060: N = 102, 472 x 589.49 L = 60.40 million L
       Unsustainable about 2060
       These calculations are also provided as a spreadsheet on the Teacher's Digital Edition

© 2017 **BIOZONE** International
ISBN: 978-1-927309-28-5
Photocopying Prohibited

188. Human Impact on the Ocean (page 278)
1. (a)-(c) any three of in any order:
   - Decline in species diversity and numbers in the oceans (across all taxa), e.g. through whaling, overfishing, and impact of ballast pollution. Some fish stocks are commercially extinct.
   - Pollution, e.g. from plastic, dumping from ships, and land runoff, kills or contaminates marine species and destroys habitat.
   - Sea bed mining and drilling destroys benthic habitats and kills benthic organisms. Spills or leakages pollute marine environments with far-reaching effects.
   - Spread of invasive species through ballast discharge can result in the displacement of native populations of marine organisms. Species that settle on hard surfaces (e.g. bryozoans, molluscs, and crustaceans such as barnacles) are particularly at risk.

189. Overfishing (page 279)
1. Overfishing takes more fish than can be replaced by normal recruitment of young fish. Overfished populations therefore show a progressive decline in growth rate and thus in population size, until there are too few fish of reproductive age to maintain the population at a level to sustain the fish take.

2. (a) Total catch rate has declined and is now nearly 300 000 tonnes less than during peak harvests in the 1970s. Mortality increased to a peak around 1990-2000 but has steadily declined since then. Spawning and recruitment rates have both declined dramatically. Spawning stock biomass has recovered slightly since 2005.
   (b) There will be little effect on stock recovery. This measure will only slow its decline, rather than increase numbers. This is because the current estimated maximum mortality rate is 0.2, lower than the fisheries target of 0.4.

190. Sustainable Fishing (page 281)
11. 76%

2. (a) Bycatch refers to the fish and other marine organisms that are caught but not wanted and so discarded.
   (b) Changes to hook design and devices (pingers) to frighten away non-target species can help reduce bycatch.

3. MSY is the maximum number or tonnage of fish that can be taken without affecting the future stock biomass and replacement rate (population growth rate).

4. (a) To determine MSY researchers would need to know the population size, age structure, and replacement rate.
   (b) Non-breeding: 3.5 million – 1.8 million = 1.7 million
   (c) No because they are the breeding recruits for the subsequent years' biomass.
   (d) Ideally, fishers should use a method to catch only the smallest of the larger (mature) fish. This is not achievable with current technology, so fishers are most likely to take the largest fish and the fish population will suffer large fertility losses as a result. The fishery is difficult to fish sustainably and not viable in the long term unless managed very carefully.

5. A catch over the MSY will be unsustainable. Reproductive individuals will not be able to compensate (by breeding) for the loss of biomass and the stock will collapse.

6. (a) At about 5 or 6 years, being the point where stock numbers are still moderately high, total fish biomass is high, and individuals are of an intermediate size (relative to maximum achievable size). If the few, older (larger) individuals are taken, the population quickly becomes skewed towards younger fish with lower reproductive capacity.
   (b) 0-6 years
   (c) Longevity, age at which reproduction begins, and mortality at different life stages.

7. Students' response. The students will decide if they think fish farming will be helpful or not helpful in stopping overfishing or mitigating its effects.
   Some justifications for fish farming may include:

- Comparison of efficiency of weight gain in fish farms vs wild.
- Fish farming meets consumer demand and allows wild stocks to recover.
- A higher proportion of food used to feed farmed fish now comes from sources other than the ocean.

Some justifications against fish farming may include:
- Waste from the fish farm enters the local ecosystem
- Disease can be problematic in fish farming.
- Heavy metals and toxins can build up in fish flesh, potentially causing health problems for the human consumer.
- Farmed fish have lower genetic diversity than wild fish.
- A considerable proportion of fish food comes from fish meal (manufactured from the catch of bait fish, which are important in marine food chains).

191. The Greenhouse Effect (page 284)
1. A greenhouse gas is a gas in the atmosphere that causes the retention of heat in the atmosphere.

2. The greenhouse effect is the retention of heat from the Sun by the Earth's atmosphere, which keeps the Earth's mean surface temperature at ~15°.

3. (a) Carbon dioxide: 41.2% increase
   (b) Methane: 156.6% increase
   (c) Nitrous oxide: 20.0% increase

4. Water is often left out of greenhouse gas table as the amount of water vapour in the atmosphere is related to temperature and therefore dependent on other greenhouse gases.

192. Climate Change (page 285)
1. Increased levels of carbon dioxide, methane, and nitrous oxides act as additional thermal blankets around the Earth, allowing the sun's energy to reach the Earth's surface, but preventing the heat escaping. This means that the Earth slowly heats up. **Note**: The atmospheric concentrations of these gases have increased dramatically above pre-industrial levels since 1750. These levels are considerably higher than at any time during the last 650,000 years (the period for which reliable data has been extracted from ice cores) and are correlated with a rise in global temperature and documented sea level rises. While correlation does not mean cause and effect, the majority of climate scientists accept the theory that the increase in anthropogenic greenhouse gas emissions is causing the rise in the Earth's temperature.

2 (a) CO_2 levels increased sharply shortly afterwards.
   (b) The invention and mass use of the steam engine to provide mechanical power saw huge amounts of coal being burned to fuel them, raising atmospheric CO_2 levels.

3. Models must be revised to take account of changing climatic conditions, new information (changing inputs), better computing power, and the development of more complex models (incorporating more variables) that more realistically describe and predict climate change scenarios.

4. Students own research and arguments. Students need to take into account the accuracy of sceptical arguments, including the data used and its source.

193. The History of Climate Modelling (page 287)
1. Ocean effects first added in the early 1990s.

2. Eruptions reduce observed temperatures (see the plot of historical data).

3. (a) Climate models have become increasingly sophisticated and complex over time (by adding in more factors affecting the climate) as computing power and our knowledge about the factors affecting climate systems have increased.
   (b) The significance of the increased complexity has been an increase in the accuracy with which climate models can predict future climate.

4. (a) Scientists enter past data (what we know) into the model and see how well the model predicts the climate changes that have already occurred.
   (b) Doing this gives greater confidence that the model is capable of accurate predictions.

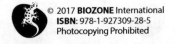

(c) The model is very accurate for the period 1960-2000 and follows the actual climate fluctuations closely over that period. Prior to 1960, trends are similar but the average of the model shows more fluctuation than actually occurred.

5. Student's own responses but some guidelines below:

(a) **Atmosphere**: Climate is governed by the global pattern of air movements. Changes in cloud cover, water vapour, and gas concentrations alter the Earth's energy balance (often called radiative forcing) and affect the Earth's climate systems. To determine how climate systems respond to any particular change in energy in the atmosphere, scientists need to understand atmospheric processes, including atmospheric feedbacks involving changes in water vapour concentrations and cloud distributions.

Oceans: The oceans are vast. Water vapour evaporated from the ocean surface provides latent heat energy to the atmosphere and drives precipitation. Most of the thermal energy at the Earth surface is stored in the oceans. The large thermal inertia of the oceans is a key factor in moderating Earth's climate. Because the oceans have such a large heat capacity and can transfer heat around the globe, it is vital to couple atmosphere and ocean models in order to simulate climate variability and changes (e.g. as in El Niño).

Ice sheets and sea ice: Sea ice is an active component of the climate system and, at high latitudes, varies greatly in extent with the seasons. In the Arctic, the sea ice is confined by the continents around it and mean sea ice thickness is 3–4 m. Around Antarctica, the sea ice is unimpeded and spreads out extensively, and the mean thickness is typically 1–2 m. Sea ice caps the ocean and interferes with exchanges of heat, water vapour, and other gases between the ocean and atmosphere. Melting sea ice freshens the ocean and reduces its density. It also changes the surface albedo reflecting heat and keeping the Earth cooler. Diminished sea ice leads to the ice-albedo positive feedback that amplifies initial loss. Diminished sea ice also increases moisture fluxes into the atmosphere, which may increase fog and low cloud and change energy balance.

Biogeochemical cycles: Biogeochemical cycles involve the fluxes of chemical elements among the Earth's systems. They are termed cscles because matter is conserved and because elements move to and from major pools via two-way fluxes, although some elements may be stored and be effectively inaccessible for long periods of time. Biogeochemical processes control atmospheric concentrations of the main greenhouse gases (CO_2, CH_4 and N_2O). Currently, more carbon is being added to the atmosphere than can be stored or taken up by ecosystems. Other elements and compounds directly and indirectly affect the carbon balance, e.g. nitrogen directly stimulates carbon uptake and indirectly decreases the soil methane sink. Changes in biogeochemical cycles of carbon, nitrogen, phosphorus, and other elements can affect concentrations of greenhouse gases in the atmosphere and alter how the planet absorbs and reflects sunlight (heat balance). There are complex feedback effects here too, because the biogeochemical cycles themselves change in response to changes in climate. For example, as soils warm, the rate of decomposition will increase, adding more CO_2 to the atmosphere. However, that same increase in decomposition accelerates the release of reactive nitrogen (and phosphorus) from organic matter, which in turn can fuel additional plant growth. Such feedback cycles can create instability that increases the vulnerability of biodiversity and human sustainability. Biogeochemical cycles are intimately connected to the activity of the biosphere (see next point).

Biosphere: The activity of organisms is central to carbon fluxes and the cycling of other elements through the Earth's systems. Photosynthetic organisms capture atmospheric CO_2 convert it to organic matter, then release of CO_2 back to the atmosphere (through respiration and decay). Microorganisms produce and oxidise methane, reduce and oxidise sulfur, and are involved in nitrogen transformations. As above, feedback effects operate, in which warming climate can accelerate decomposition

(adding CO_2 to the atmosphere) but can also drive increased plant growth (removing atmospheric CO_2). Revegetation of some deforested lands, e.g. second growth forests in the US, is helping to store more carbon, but this storage amount is small relative to the amount being added to the atmosphere through human activity.

Human activity: The mobilisation of carbon, nitrogen, and phosphorus from the Earth's crust and atmosphere into the environment by human activity has increased 36, 9, and 13 times respectively compared to pre-industrial times. Fossil fuel burning, land-cover change, production of cement, and fertiliser extraction and production are major causes of these increases. CO_2 production dominates atmospheric forcing of global climate change but methane is also important. It the most abundant non-CO_2 greenhouse gas, and is 20-30 times more potent than CO_2 over a century timescale. It accounted for 9% of all human-caused greenhouse gas emissions in the US in 2011, and there is now more than twice as much in the atmosphere than in pre-industrial times (GlobalChange.gov). Even in light of the complexity of climate models and their inherent assumptions and errors, the evidence is overwhelming that human activity is responsible for current warming. Atmospheric CO_2 concentrations are higher than they have been in over 800 000 years and the current observable increase is more than 100 times faster than that experienced at the end of the last ice age (NOAA). This is termed human forcing and it will drive climate change into the future, even if emissions stop now. How do we know humans are responsible? When climate models include only recorded natural climate drivers, such as the sun's intensity, the models cannot accurately reproduce the observed warming of the past half century. When human-induced climate drivers are also included in the models, then they accurately capture recent temperature increases in the atmosphere and in the oceans. Moreover, the lower-level atmosphere, which contains the carbon load, is expanding. Modelling the effect of human activity accurately into the future will depend on obtaining accurate predictions of emissions. Even with global cooperation for reduction, continuing warming is inevitable. Climate change predictions include:

– On average, Earth will become warmer. Not all regions will be warmer however.
– Warmer conditions will probably lead to more evaporation and precipitation overall, but individual regions will vary.
– A stronger greenhouse effect will warm the oceans and partially melt glaciers and other ice, increasing sea level. Ocean water also will expand as it warms, contributing further to sea level rise.
– Some crop yields may increase, but the regions where current crops can be grown will change. Natural patterns of biodiversity will shift.

External influences: Many climate drivers influence global climate, including changes in solar intensity and volcanic eruptions, as well as changes to atmospheric greenhouse gases. Evidence shows that solar variability has played a role in past climate changes, e.g. decreased solar activity is thought to have triggered the Little Ice Age between approximately 1650 and 1850, when Greenland was largely cut off by ice from 1410 to the 1720s and glaciers advanced in the Alps. However, several lines of evidence show that current global warming cannot be explained by changes in energy from the sun (NASA):

– Since 1750, the average amount of energy coming from the sun either remained constant or increased slightly.
– If the warming were caused by a more active sun, then scientists would expect to see warmer temperatures in all layers of the atmosphere. Instead, they have observed a cooling in the upper atmosphere, and a warming at the surface and in the lower parts of the atmosphere. That's because greenhouse gases are trapping heat in the lower atmosphere.
– Climate models that include solar irradiance changes can't reproduce the observed temperature trend over the past century or more without including a rise in greenhouse gases.

(b) Students' own decisions.

194. Models of Climate Change (page 289)

1. Running different climate change scenarios (i.e. scenarios assuming different inputs) enables scientists to generate best case and worst case scenarios and plan accordingly.

2. (a) The A2 scenario
   (b) High population growth and high energy use without a correspondingly high rate of technological and economic growth (to limit carbon foot print).
   (c) Scenario B assumes sustainable development: low population growth, high technological and economic advancement, and low energy use (reduced emissions). The areas devoted to agriculture and reforestation increases (increased carbon storage).
   (d) The 2001 and 2012 models are very similar for the A2 scenario (high population growth, high energy use, low technological advancement) but the projections for the A1B and B1 scenarios are more optimistic in the 2012 models compared to the 2001 models (less temperature change). Moreover, predictions for B1 and A1B scenarios are more similar to each other in the 2012 models than in the earlier models.

3. (a) Sea level rise is caused by the thermal expansion of water as it warms and melting of glaciers and sea ice.
   (b) Almost 40% of the US population lives directly on the shoreline and this figure is expected to increase by 8% by 2020. These communities are very vulnerable to sea level rise because coastal regions are at high risk of inundation.

4. (a) 0.1-0.2 cm per year = 1-2 mm per year.
   (b) Sea level rise has been 3.2 mm per year so between 1.5 and 3 times greater.
   (c) Increase in global average temperature, leading to thermal expansion of sea water and melting of ice sheets.

5. (a) The graph shows prediction for global sea level rise based on different climate modelling scenarios.
   (b) Worst case scenario predicts a sea level rise of 200 cm (2 m) above the 1992 arbitrary zero by 2100.
   (c) Best case scenario predicts a sea level rise of ~20 cm (0.2 m) above the 1992 arbitrary zero by 2100.

195. Climate Change and Effects on Biodiversity (page 291)

1. (a) Global warming will result in an increased frequency of weather extremes (floods, droughts etc) and a loss of land as coastal areas are inundated. Erosion rates may also increase as a result. Glacial retreats will reduce water supplies and snow lines will increase in altitude. Climate changes may shift the governing physical environment in certain regions (and consequently cause a shift in predominant vegetation). Ocean pH will also fall as a result of CO_2 absorption (again, with consequent changes in biotic communities).
   (b) Depending on the crop involved, growing range may shrink, expand, or shift. Crop plants may be affected more by higher night temperatures than by higher daytime temperatures. High night temperatures affect the ability of some crop plants such as rice to set seed and fruit. This will cause a reduction in yield, and so also a decrease in the amount of seed available.
   (c) Farmers may adjust by planting different crops in some areas, e.g. crops that are able to grow and set seed at higher temperatures. New crop strains may be able to be developed for the higher temperature ranges.
   (d) Migratory birds in the northern hemisphere are now not travelling as far south during the winter months (as higher latitudes become more hospitable) and they are making their migrations north up to two weeks earlier than usual.
   (e) Birds may arrive at feeding grounds before the main food supply is ready. Plants with daylength-dependent flowering may not yet be flowering and therefore insects (and seeds and fruits) may not be plentiful enough to feed the migrants. While the distribution of food resources may remain the same, the birds are not migrating as far south and may be disconnected from their winter food supplies.
   (f) As air temperatures rise, so too does the snow line in alpine areas. Animals living on or above the snow line

will be forced into smaller areas. If they are unable to move to higher latitudes where the snow line is lower, it is inevitable that they will become extinct in their native ranges as they run out of food and space.

2. Evidence suggests that insect populations will be affected by global warming. Plant fossil data shows that browse damage peaked during past thermal maxima, suggesting that insect populations will increase in size as temperatures rise.

196. Climate Change and Agriculture (page 293)

1. Some crops (e.g. wheat, rice and soybeans) may benefit the higher temperatures and CO_2 levels. They may have longer growing seasons or their growing region may expand. Other crops may be harmed by global warming. These include crops that are already being grown near their climate thresholds (e.g. in equatorial regions). Crop plants may be affected more by higher night temperatures than by higher daytime temperatures because high night temperatures affect the ability of some crop plants such as rice to set seed and fruit.

2. Climate change may allow pest species to expand their habitable range and affect a wider range of crops over a wider area. Evidence for this comes from the fossil record. It shows that global temperatures increased 56 mya (the Palaeocene-Eocene Thermal Maximum). Fossils of insect browse damage from this time show that insect damage peaked at the same time, suggesting insect populations will increase in size as temperatures rise.

197. Climate Change and Effects on the Arctic (page 294)

1. Low sea-ice albedo and area cause more heat to be absorbed by the land and sea, causing the ocean's water to warm more during the summer and take longer to cool during the autumn. Winter sea-ice then takes longer to form and is thinner. Thin sea-ice has a lower albedo than thick sea-ice and melts faster in the spring leading to even less sea-ice the following winter. Thus thin ice and small area cover causes even thinner and less cover the following year in a potentially perpetual cycle until the sea-ice is lost.

2. Polar animals that live out on the sea-ice will be directly affected as the area covered by sea-ice reduces. Polar bears which hunt out on the ice find it harder to find food and must swim longer distances to firm ice. The reduction of sea-ice cover may also affect species that live below the ice as more light and heat will penetrate the waters and to deeper depths.

198. Temperature and the Distribution of Species (page 295)

1. Species distribution of *Rana* is closely related to water temperature (mating and embryonic development for each species occurs within a certain temperature range). Increasing global temperatures may result in a northwards shift of some species as their preferred water temperature shifts. Those frogs that are furthest north (*R. sylvatica*) may end up with a reduced range, while those further south (*R. clamintans*) may increase their range, depending on available habitat.

2. Climate change may cause changes in temperature enough that species may be able to (or have to) change where they live. Populations of animals in cooler climates may be forced north in the Northern Hemisphere, while species from warmer climates may expanded their ranges further north and south from the equator.

199. Ocean Acidification (page 296)

1. (a) Ocean acidification describes the decline in the pH of ocean waters towards a less alkaline state.
   (b) Ocean acidification makes it harder for shell making organisms to obtain the carbonate ions they need to build shells causing them to have thinner or deformed shells.

2. (a) Since the 1850s the pH of the oceans has been declining.
   (b) A rise in atmospheric CO_2 level. CO_2 dissolves into water forming carbonic acid, which lowers the pH.

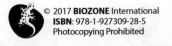

© 2017 **BIOZONE** International
ISBN: 978-1-927309-28-5
Photocopying Prohibited

200. Technological Solutions to Climate Change
(page 297)

1. All three types of carbon capture solutions recover the CO_2 so that it can be stored and used for other purposes. Pre-combustion capture captures the CO_2 before combustion by gasifying the coal and recovering the CO_2 before burning the hydrogen. Post combustion capture recovers the CO_2 released by combustion, washing it from the flue gas and regasifying and compressing it for storage. Oxyfuel combustion uses oxygen in the furnace, producing only CO_2 in the flue gas, which is collected for storage.

2. Captured CO_2 can be compressed and put to use, e.g. for inflation or use in making carbonated beverages. It can also be injected into porous rock strata and trapped between non-porous layers. Even if CO_2 has to be transported to the injection well, this still produces less CO_2 than is captured. CO_2 can also be injected into depleted oil wells or other geological formation, released into deep ocean waters (below 1000 m where it is isolated from the atmosphere), or solidified (and made inert). CO_2 may also be used as a starter for synthetic fuels.

3. Injection of CO_2 into rock strata for depleted wells carries the risk that large volumes of CO_2 will be released if the rock is unstable. This would kill animal life in the area. Deep ocean storage will alter ocean chemistry in the region of storage and risk immediate kills of ocean life and lowering of ocean pH over time. This would be harmful to the health and longevity of corals and shell-forming organisms. Deep ocean storage would require transport of CO_2 to the site and has not yet been deployed or demonstrated.

4. (a) 4.1 billion tonnes.
   (b) CO_2 is produced at two points in cement manufacture (1) when fossil fuels are burned to heat $CaCO_3$ to ~1400°C and (2) from the heat-induced degradation of the $CaCO_3$.
   (c) It is carbon negative because it absorbs more CO_2 than is produced during its manufacture.
   (d) 4.1 billion x 0.6 = 2.46 billion tonnes

201. Supporting Conservation Through Legislation
(page 299)

1. (a) Rio Convention objectives: Conserve biodiversity, sustainable use of biodiversity, and fair and equitable sharing of the benefits arising from genetic resources.
   (b) CITES objectives: Ensure that the trade in plants and animals does not threaten their survival in the wild.

2. The WWF focuses on the conservation of biodiversity and reduction of humanity's ecological footprint. Areas of focus include climate, food, forests, freshwater, oceans, and policy influence. It achieves these aims through convincing governments to adopt and enforce environmentally friendly policies, often by making public information about the possible negative impacts of proposed activities, such as mining.

202. Chapter Review (page 300)
No model answer. Summary is the student's own.

203. KEY TERMS AND IDEAS: Did You Get It? (page 302)

1. abiotic factor (D), biotic factor (H), carbon cycle (G), competition (F), conservation (K), ecological pyramid (I), nitrogen cycle (E), nutrient cycle (M), primary succession (L), quadrat (C), secondary succession (J), transect (A), trophic level (B).

2. (a) Primary production decreases with depth.
   (b) Photosynthesis occurs in the photic zone. Producers in the photic zone provide the basis of the marine food chain (most of the primary and higher order consumers), so most marine life is found here.

3. Corn: producer
   Mouse: 1st order (primary) consumer
   Corn snake: 2nd order (secondary) consumer
   Hawk: 3rd order (tertiary) consumer

4. Student's own research and opinion. Students need to look at the validity and bias of the information and sources when formulating an opinion.

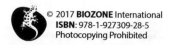 © 2017 **BIOZONE** International
ISBN: 978-1-927309-28-5
Photocopying Prohibited

NOTES

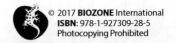